Oxford Chemistry Series

General Editors
P. W. ATKINS   J. S. E. HOLKER   A. K. HOLLIDAY

Oxford Chemistry Series

JOHN ALBERY
FELLOW OF UNIVERSITY COLLEGE, OXFORD

Electrode kinetics

Clarendon Press · Oxford · 1975

Oxford University Press, Ely House, London W.1

GLASGOW   NEW YORK   TORONTO   MELBOURNE   WELLINGTON
CAPE TOWN   IBADAN   NAIROBI   DAR ES SALAAM   LUSAKA   ADDIS ABABA
DELHI   BOMBAY   CALCUTTA   MADRAS   KARACHI   LAHORE   DACCA
KUALA LUMPUR   SINGAPORE   HONG KONG   TOKYO

SBN 0 19 8554338

© OXFORD UNIVERSITY PRESS 1975

PRINTED IN GREAT BRITAIN BY
J. W. ARROWSMITH LTD., BRISTOL, ENGLAND

Editor's foreword

The migration of an electron from an electrode to an electrolyte solution is an important part of an electrochemical process. We know roughly how ions behave in a bulk solution and we know roughly how electrons behave in a bulk metal electrode: in the present volume we are concerned with the problem of the interface. In the study of the kinetics of processes at electrodes we are able to explore the nature of the solution in the vicinity of the electrode and to construct models of its behaviour. Whereas temperature changes are the lever with which conventional chemical reactants are lifted over potential barriers, in electrode kinetics we possess a new, powerful, easily controlled lever: the potential of the electrode. Our control of this potential gives us power to speed or slow reactions over an enormous range of velocities. The transfer of an electron is a fundamental chemical process: electron transfer between molecules is a fundamental step of a variety of chemical reactions in solution, and both analysis and synthesis benefit from a knowledge of its rate and mechanism.

The behaviour of ions in bulk solution is described by Robbins in *Ions in solution* (2): *an introduction to electrochemistry* (OCS 2), and their chemical behaviour is described by Pass in *Ions in solution* (3): *inorganic properties* (OCS 7). The basic theory of chemical rate processes, on which much of the discussion in the present book hinges, is described in Pilling's *Reaction kinetics* (OCS 22), and the chemical thermodynamics, particularly the concepts of free energy and chemical potential, are to be found in Smith's *Basic chemical thermodynamics* (OCS 8). The statistical mechanical concepts are introduced in Gasser and Richard's *Entropy and energy levels* (OCS 19). Surfaces are of immense technological importance in industry, and apart from the obvious connexion of the material of this book with electrochemical syntheses and power generation from fuel cells, there is a deeper connexion with the general theory of catalysis: see Bond's *Heterogeneous catalysis: principles and applications* (OCS 18).

P.W.A.

Preface

DISTASTE and disgust are the predominant emotions that the normal student feels for electrochemistry. The Pogendorff potentiometer, the normal calomel electrode, liquid junction potentials, reversible and irreversible cells, all seem to him to have been invented by the Holy Office for the torturing of innocent students. As the train of old bearded electrochemists passes on its way, muttering of Galvani potentials and murmuring orisons for Guggenheim, the student escapes from cells without transference and relaxes with a little spin–orbit coupling.

This is a pity. Fig. 0.1 depicts the Ptolemaic view of electrode kinetics. (For the sake of clarity we have omitted the complicated system of epicycles which enable most chemists to remain in perpetual orbit around the subject.) There are many important applications for which an understanding of electrode kinetics is essential; they include corrosion, fuel cells, new batteries for electric cars, and analytical techniques for measuring pollution. But particularly important in view of the depletion of fossil fuels is the contribution that electrochemistry can, and must, make to energy storage and conversion. Photoelectrochemical cells should be capable of collecting solar energy; its storage and utilization will require better and more efficient batteries. As nuclear power replaces fossil fuels industrial processes will be carried out most efficiently by the sequence:

$$\text{Nuclear power} \rightarrow \text{Generation of electricity} \rightarrow \text{Electrochemical synthesis}$$

However despite the importance of these applications this book is concerned with the top half of Fig. 0.1 rather than the bottom half. This is because I am most concerned to show how electrode kinetics is linked to other more familiar topics. It is easier and I hope more rewarding to get to, and study, Clapham Junction rather than travel to the end of a picturesque but deserted branch line. Thus I hope that, after reading this book, students will not in future regard electrode kinetics as a remote and difficult subject but will see it more as a link between many different topics in thermodynamics, kinetics, photochemistry, inorganic redox systems, and physical organic chemistry.

Given a book of this length, I had to choose between attempting an aerial survey of the whole of electrode kinetics or working through in more detail some of the more important lines of argument. I have chosen to do the latter since the descriptive approach may 'tell it how it is' but must always be authoritarian. The student has to accept my word that it is so. The more detailed approach allows one to share the argument. Many of these arguments are mathematical in nature and indeed on first impression this book may seem

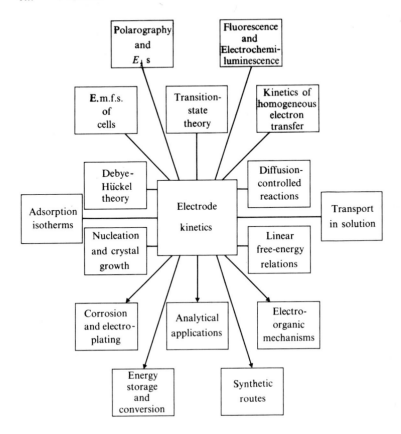

Fig. 0.1. The Ptolemaic view of electrode kinetics.

to have a large number of equations. It has, and the reason is that there is nothing more infuriating than to be told that 'it can easily be shown that' and to find that 'easily' means two days, a ream of foolscap, and the help of a member of the department of mathematics. I hope that I have included enough lines in the argument and enough appendices for the mathematics to be reasonably easy to follow. Certainly no great mathematical skills are required. Providing you can integrate you can cope. If you can't, there are still nearly as many pictures as equations.

Chapters 1, 3, and 5 are the main line of the argument and on a first reading Chapters 2 and 4 could well be omitted. Indeed, having written Chapter 2, I almost left it out myself, but the theory of the double layer is closely connected with Debye–Hückel theory; it is easier to think of the electrode and its ionic atmosphere than the mutual effect of one ion upon another. Also double layers are important not only in electrode kinetics, but also in colloids and biological interfaces. Hence on general grounds the chapter has remained. Chapter 4 describes a simplified view of the Marcus and Levich theories of electron transfer reactions. This is an important class of reactions firstly because they are the means by which oxidation states are changed and secondly because they lie mid-way between other reactions studied in chemical kinetics and electronic transitions studied in spectroscopy.

I apologize to my electrochemical brethren for not including their favourite branch line or describing in detail their own wayside halt. In particular I have said almost nothing about adsorption, corrosion, fused salts, or electro-crystallization. This is not to say that these topics are unimportant. But the mechanisms involved are more complicated than those described in this book. Thus they will have to wait for another book and another author, more knowledgeable than I.

I wish to thank my pupils and students and in particular Alan Davis and Jon Hadgraft for their helpful comments, Peter Atkins as editor of the series for combining aggressive patience with tempered criticism, and above all Mrs. Elizabeth Price who, without the aid of the Rosetta stone, managed to type the manuscript.

This book is dedicated to my tutor, Professor R. P. Bell, F.R.S. Following the success of his *magnum opus*, I was tempted to call it *The electron in chemistry*, but perhaps that might have led to prosecution under the Trade Descriptions Act.

University College, Oxford   W.J.A.

Contents

1. Potential-dependent rate constants

Introduction

WE start by considering the electrode–solution interface, for electrode kinetics is the study of the rates of reaction of charged particles at the interface between a solid and a liquid solution. Traditionally the solid has been a metal. A metal has the great advantage that it offers only a low resistance to the current caused by the flow of charged particles at the interface. The liquid is usually an ionic solution since again the current must flow through the solution. In this book we shall concentrate on water as the solvent since more work has been carried out in water than in other solvents or in molten salts. Hence we confine ourselves to a metal electrode in contact with an aqueous solution. There are now two types of charged particle that may cross the interface:

(1) a metal ion;
(2) an electron.

Sugar/tea system

Let us consider first the metal ion and imagine that as in Fig. 1.1 we have a silver electrode connected to earth in contact with a solution containing Ag^+. For comparison there is also a mug of sweet tea with a sugar lump connected to nothing.

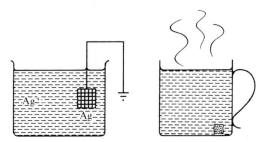

FIG. 1.1. A silver electrode and a sweet cup of tea.

Now in the case of the sugar at the interface some molecules will be leaving the sugar lump and some will be being deposited on it from the solution. So we may write:

$$j = k'_0 - k'_1 [\text{sugar}]_0 \qquad (1.1)$$

where

j is the flux of sugar from the lump into the tea

k_0' is a rate constant describing the dissolution process

k_1' is a rate constant describing the deposition of the sugar

and

[sugar]$_0$ is the concentration of sugar in the solution at the surface of the lump measured in moles m^{-3}.

The flux j is the number of moles passing through unit area in unit time and for our purposes is measured in mol m^{-2} s^{-1}. The rate constant k_0' must have the same dimensions. The rate constants are primed to show that they describe processes happening on a surface and to distinguish them from the familiar unprimed k used to describe reactions occurring in the bulk of the solution. The rate constant k_1' has the rather peculiar dimensions of m s^{-1}. This is because we have to relate a flux per unit area in terms of a concentration per unit volume. This is also the reason why we shall describe concentrations in terms of mol m^{-3} rather than the more usual units of mol dm^{-3}; for the old-fashioned 1 mol m^{-3} is the same as 1 mM (millimolar).

Strictly speaking we should include an activity coefficient in eqn (1.1). However the inclusion of γs, fs, or curly brackets, although pleasing to the purist, makes the equations appear more complicated. Since the inclusion is not essential for our understanding of the fundamentals of electrode kinetics we will deal only with the simpler equations which describe ideal behaviour.

Finally we include a subscript of 0 on [sugar]$_0$ since the rate depends on the concentration of sugar at the surface of the lump. This concentration may not be the same as the concentration in the bulk of the solution designated [sugar]$_\infty$. For instance if the lump has just been added to fresh tea then

$$[\text{sugar}]_0 > [\text{sugar}]_\infty = 0.$$

The sugar will be diffusing (before the tea is stirred) from the lump into the rest of the tea.

If enough sugar is added, eventually the tea becomes saturated. Then the flux at the surface of the lump will be zero and the sugar concentration is uniform:

$$[\text{sugar}]_0 = [\text{sugar}]_\infty = k_0'/k_1'. \tag{1.2}$$

The term k_0'/k_1' describes the solubility of the sugar at whatever temperature the tea has now reached.

Ag$^+$/Ag system

Now let us see what happens when we turn to the Ag$^+$. The sugar can exist either in the lattice of the lump or in the tea. Similarly Ag$^+$ can exist either in the metallic lattice where it is said to be surrounded by a 'sea of delocalized electrons' or it can exist as a solvated ion surrounded by a sea of water molecules. Thus we can write eqn (1.3) which is the exact counterpart of (1.1).

$$j_{\text{Ag}^+} = k_0' - k_1'[\text{Ag}^+]_0. \tag{1.3}$$

But the difference between Ag^+ and sugar is that the Ag^+ is charged while the sugar is neutral. Thus the potential difference between the metal and solution will affect the rates at which Ag^+ crosses the interface. The more negative the potential of the solution with respect to that of the metal the faster the Ag^+ will move from the metal to the solution and at the same time the harder it will be for the Ag^+ to be incorporated into the metal lattice from the solution. Qualitatively we can therefore write:†

$$(E_{\text{soln}} - E_{\text{metal}}) \downarrow \quad \text{or} \quad (E_{\text{metal}} - E_{\text{soln}}) \uparrow, \quad k'_0 \uparrow \text{ and } k'_1 \downarrow .$$

No such considerations arise in the case of the sugar system. That is why electrode kinetics is concerned with the movement of charged particles across the interface. Although the charge on the particles increases the complexity of the problem, the fact that the rate constants depend on the potential difference at the interface and can therefore be altered by twiddling a knob is an essential distinguishing feature of electrode kinetics.

Effect of potential on rate constants

We now move from a qualitative description to a more quantitative one. Consider the system,

$$Ag_S^+ + e_{M^-} \underset{k'_0}{\overset{k'_1}{\rightleftarrows}} Ag_M.$$

The subscripts S and M indicate solution and metal respectively. Like any other reaction as the Ag^+ transfers from the solution to the lattice and vice versa it will have to surmount a free energy barrier. When the ion is in neither the electronic nor the aqueous 'sea' its free energy is larger. Fig. 1.2 shows a

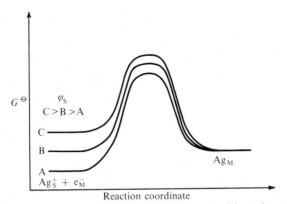

FIG. 1.2. Plot of free energy barriers against reaction coordinate for $Ag_S^+ + e_M^- \rightleftarrows Ag_M$ at three different potentials, showing three slices of Fig. 1.3.

† See Robbins, *Ions in solution (2): an introduction to electrochemistry* (OCS2) for a discussion of the electrode potentials and the significance of their sign.

barrier in the free energy. It could have been taken from any text book on chemical kinetics,† except that in our case the free energy surface depends on the potential and therefore there has to be a curve for each potential difference. This is shown in Fig. 1.3 where $G^{\ominus}$ is plotted as a function of both the reaction coordinate and the potential. Remember that in Fig. 1.1 the metal was connected to earth so that its potential does not change. As the potential of the solution increases the Ag_S^+ becomes less stable. The line OP describes the effect on the free energy of the Ag_S^+ of this change of potential. Because $F\phi_S$ is the energy of 1 mol of singly-charged positive ions in a potential ϕ_S the change in free energy‡ is

$$G^{\ominus} = \text{constant} + F\phi_S$$

for Ag^+, and in general

$$G^{\ominus} = \text{constant} + nF\phi_S \tag{1.4}$$

where n is the charge number of the particle being considered.

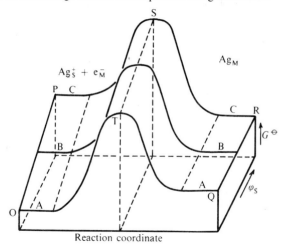

FIG. 1.3. Free energy surface showing variation of free energy with reaction coordinate and ϕ_S, the potential of the solution when the electrode is connected to earth, for $Ag_S^+ + e_M^- \rightleftarrows Ag_M$.

Now the lines OP and QR describe the free energies of the stable states of the Ag^+; to describe the kinetics we have to consider the line TS, describing the change in free energy of the transition state, with respect to the change in potential difference. The gradient of this line is less than that of OP since as

---

† It was in fact taken from Pilling's *Reaction kinetics* (OCS 22) which discusses elementary and modern aspects of the subject.

‡ See Smith's *Basic chemical thermodynamics* (OCS 8) for a discussion of the concept of Gibbs Free Energy and its chemical significance.

we move from left to right in Fig. 1.2 the surfaces converge; they are well separated on the left hand side of the diagram and on top of each other on the right hand side. Thus the transition state is less sensitive to changes in potential than the Ag_S^+. We can write

$$G_{\ddagger}^{\ominus} = \text{constant} + \beta n F \phi_S \qquad (1.5)$$

where $n = +1$ for Ag^+. The parameter β is called the *transfer coefficient*; it is often approximately equal to $\frac{1}{2}$, which corresponds to the gradient of TS being half way between the gradients of OP and QR.

Now in ordinary chemical kinetics one writes from transition-state theory†
that

$$k = \frac{k_B T}{h} \exp\left(-\frac{\Delta G_{\ddagger}}{RT}\right)$$

or

$$\ln k = \ln\left(\frac{k_B T}{h}\right) - \frac{\Delta G_{\ddagger}}{RT},$$

where k_B is the Boltzmann constant with subscript B to distinguish it from k, a rate constant.

So by exactly the same arguments we write for the heterogeneous rate constants k':

$$k' = Z' \exp\left(\frac{-\Delta G_{\ddagger}}{RT}\right)$$

or

$$\ln k' = \ln Z' - \frac{\Delta G_{\ddagger}}{RT}. \qquad (1.6)$$

The frequency factor Z' is different since it has to describe the reactions of molecules with a plane surface and has dimensions of $m\,s^{-1}$. We will discuss it at a later stage. For the moment combining (1.5) with (1.6) we obtain for the process

$$Ag_M \xrightarrow{k'_0} Ag_S^+ + e_M^-$$

$$\ln k'_0 = (\ln k'_0)_{\phi_S = 0} - \beta \frac{F\phi_S}{RT}, \qquad (1.7)$$

and for the process

$$e_M^- + Ag_S^+ \xrightarrow{k'_1} Ag_M$$

$$\ln k'_1 = (\ln k'_1)_{\phi_S = 0} + \frac{F\phi_S}{RT} - \beta \frac{F\phi_S}{RT}$$

$$= (\ln k'_1)_{\phi_S = 0} + (1 - \beta)\frac{F\phi_S}{RT} \qquad (1.8)$$

$$= (\ln k'_1)_{\phi_S = 0} + \alpha \frac{F\phi_S}{RT}.$$

† See Pilling, *loc. cit.*

While β is the transfer coefficient for an oxidation, it is helpful to define as well α the transfer coefficient for a reduction. For a single electron-transfer reaction,

$$\alpha + \beta = 1.$$

In eqn (1.7) the reactant is unaffected by changes in ϕ_S (the metal is earthed) and the term β describes the effect on the transition state. In eqn (1.8) again the β term refers to the transition state; the $F\phi_S/RT$ term describes the effect of the potential on the free energy of the reactant.

In order to simplify the discussion we have so far kept $\phi_M = 0$ by connecting the electrode to earth. This special condition can now be removed and we can write that in general:

$$\ln k_0' = (\ln k_0')_{\phi_S = \phi_M} + \frac{\beta n F(\phi_M - \phi_S)}{RT} \tag{1.9}$$

and

$$\ln k_1' = (\ln k_1')_{\phi_S = \phi_M} - \frac{(1 - \beta)n F(\phi_M - \phi_S)}{RT}. \tag{1.10}$$

Eqns (1.9) and (1.10) reduce to (1.7) and (1.8) when $\phi_M = 0$ and $n = 1$. The crucial potential is the potential *difference* at the interface. If both ϕ_M and ϕ_S are increased by one volt then there will be no difference to Fig. 1.3 since while Ag^+ will be less stable the electron will be more stable. Substitution in eqn (1.3) gives

$$j = (k_0')_{\phi_S = \phi_M} \exp\left[\frac{\beta F(\phi_M - \phi_S)}{RT}\right] - (k_1')_{\phi_S = \phi_M} \exp\left[\frac{(1 - \beta)F(\phi_M - \phi_S)}{RT}\right][Ag^+]_0$$

Nernst equation

When no current flows at the electrode $j = 0$ and

$$[Ag^+]_0 = [Ag^+]_\infty = \left(\frac{k_0'}{k_1'}\right)_{\phi_S = \phi_M} \exp\left[\frac{F(\phi_M - \phi_S)}{RT}\right]. \tag{1.11}$$

This equation may be compared with (1.2) for the sugar in the tea. The essential difference is that the 'solubility' of the Ag^+ depends upon the potential difference at the interface. Furthermore we can rearrange eqn (1.11) to obtain,

$$\phi_M - \phi_S = (\phi_M - \phi_S)_{[Ag^+]_\infty = 1} + \frac{RT}{F} \ln [Ag^+]_\infty. \tag{1.12}$$

This is just the Nernst Equation for the Ag^+/Ag half cell.† Notice that (1.11) and (1.12) do not contain the parameter α. When we put $j = 0$ we stopped the net transfer of Ag^+, abandoned the heady regions of kinetics, and descended

† See Robbins, *loc. cit.*, p. 66.

to the more mundane realm of thermodynamics. The parameter α described a property of the transition state, at the top of the free-energy barrier, and therefore has no place in the thermodynamic results (1.11) and (1.12). The Nernst equation can be derived without describing the kinetics. In order to describe the rate processes the kinetic model has to be more detailed and complicated. Thus kinetic derivations are no substitute for an understanding of thermodynamics. However it is of course necessary that the results from the special case of $j = 0$ in the kinetic argument should agree with those of thermodynamics.

Fe^{3+}/Fe^{2+} system

We now turn to the second type of electrode process in which an electron and not an ion is transferred across the interface. In this case no atoms are transferred across the interface and the material of the electrode is insoluble in the solution phase. The electrode acts as a source or sink for electrons; it is made of an inert metal, usually platinum. We begin with the simplest example, in which the electrode reaction is a single electron transfer; for example:

$$e_M^- + Fe_S^{3+} \underset{k_{-1}'}{\overset{k_1'}{\rightleftharpoons}} Fe_S^{2+}$$

Fig. 1.4 shows schematically the levels available to the electrons both in the metal and in the solution. In the metal the electronic energy levels are closely spaced; the valence electrons are delocalized over the whole lattice and to a first approximation they can be considered as a 'gas' of electrons con-

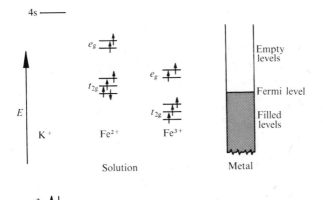

Fig. 1.4. Energy diagram (not to scale) of energy level for electrons in the metal and on ions in the solution.

strained to be inside the 'box' formed by the metallic lattice.† These closely spaced levels are filled by the electrons up to the *Fermi level*, which, by definition, is the highest occupied level. On the other hand, in the ions in solution the electrons are localized in discrete orbitals; we have shown the orbitals for the d-electrons for $Fe^{2+}(H_2O)_6$ and $Fe^{3+}(H_2O)_6$. The orbitals for Fe^{3+} lie lower than those for Fe^{2+} because of the decreased electron–electron repulsion. Electron transfer can take place from Fe^{2+} to the metal and from the metal to Fe^{3+}. We have also shown, as a contrast, K^+, an ion with an 'inert gas' structure. The large gap between 3p and 4s means that it is difficult to transfer electrons to the 4s orbitals or take them out of the 3p; hence it is difficult to reduce K^+ at an electrode and almost impossible to oxidize it.

Effect of potential

If the metal is connected to earth we can follow the same type of argument as we used in the case of Ag^+. The flux will be given by:

$$j = k_1'[Fe^{3+}]_0 - k_{-1}'[Fe^{2+}]_0.$$

Both the rate constants depend on the potential difference at the interface. Both ions become less stable as the potential of the solution is raised with respect to that of the metal; but the Fe^{3+}, having the higher charge, is affected more than the Fe^{2+}. The free-energy surface is drawn in Fig. 1.5 as a function of both the reaction coordinate and the potential of the solution ϕ_S; the potential of the metal is fixed by connecting it to earth. The lines OP and QR describe the effects of the potential ϕ_S on the free energies of the Fe^{3+} and Fe^{2+} ions respectively and we have:

$$\text{OP} \qquad G^{\ominus} = \text{constant} + 3F\phi_S,$$
$$\text{QR} \qquad G^{\ominus} = \text{constant} + 2F\phi_S.$$

Three sections across the surface at fixed ϕ_S are drawn in Fig. 1.6 firstly without shifting the energy scales and secondly after adjusting them so that the sections coincide on the right hand side. The second diagram in Fig. 1.6 now looks very similar to Fig. 1.2 and as before the gradient of the line TS is intermediate between that of OP and QR. We can write:

$$G_{\ddagger}^{\ominus} = \text{constant} + (2+\beta)F\phi_S$$

where $0 < \beta < 1$. By exactly the same arguments as we used for (1.7) and (1.8) we obtain:

$$\qquad\qquad\qquad \text{Reactant} \quad \text{Transition state}$$
$$\ln k_1' = (\ln k_1')_{\phi_S=0} + \frac{3F\phi_S}{RT} - \frac{(2+\beta)F\phi_S}{RT}$$

† A more detailed view of the metal structure is given in Atkins *Quanta* (OCS 21).

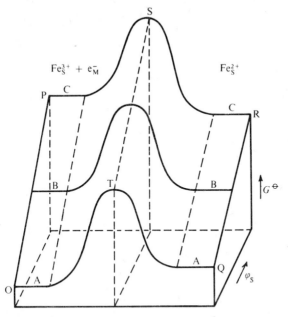

Fig. 1.5. Free energy surface showing variation of free energy with reaction coordinate and the potential of the solution, when the electrode is connected to earth, for $Fe_S^{3+} + e_M^- \rightleftarrows Fe_S^{2+}$.

and

$$\underset{\text{Reactant}}{\quad} \underset{\text{Transition state}}{\quad}$$

$$\ln k'_{-1} = (\ln k'_{-1})_{\phi_S = 0} + \frac{2F\phi_S}{RT} - \frac{(2+\beta)F\phi_S}{RT}.$$

Removing the restriction that $\phi_M = 0$ we then obtain the equivalent of (1.9) and (1.10):

$$\ln k'_1 = (\ln k'_1)_{\phi_S = \phi_M} - \frac{(1-\beta)F(\phi_M - \phi_S)}{RT} \qquad (1.13)$$

and

$$\ln k'_{-1} = (\ln k'_{-1})_{\phi_S = \phi_M} + \frac{\beta F(\phi_M - \phi_S)}{RT}. \qquad (1.14)$$

We have not included in these equations the quantity n the charge on the particle since we are dealing here with electron-transfer reactions and, as we shall see, electrons are much more likely to be transferred one at a time

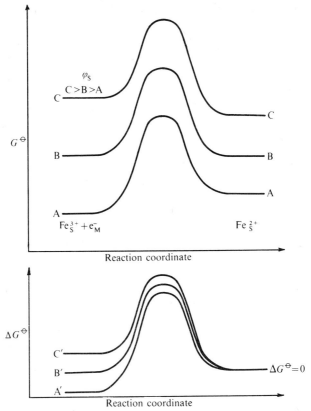

FIG. 1.6. Slices of Fig. 1.5 at constant potential. In the lower diagram the curves have been shifted so that they coincide on the right hand side ($\Delta G^{\ominus} = G^{\ominus} - G^{\ominus}$ for Fe_S^{2+}).

than in groups of two or more. Thus in general for electron-transfer reactions,

$$n = 1. \tag{1.15}$$

The equation for the flux of electrons at the electrode surface is

$$j = (k_1')_{\phi_S = \phi_M} \; \exp\left[-\frac{(1-\beta)F(\phi_M - \phi_S)}{RT}\right][Fe^{3+}]_0 -$$

$$(k_{-1}')_{\phi_S = \phi_M} \exp\left[\frac{(\beta)F(\phi_M - \phi_S)}{RT}\right][Fe^{2+}]_0. \tag{1.16}$$

We can now see what happens when $j = 0$ and no current flows. Then rearrangement of (1.16) gives

$$\phi_M - \phi_S = (\phi_M - \phi_S)_{[Fe^{3+}]_\infty = [Fe^{2+}]_\infty} + \frac{RT}{F} \ln \frac{[Fe^{3+}]_\infty}{[Fe^{2+}]_\infty}. \tag{1.17}$$

This is again the Nernst equation for the Fe^{3+}/Fe^{2+} half cell.

In this book we shall be more concerned with this second type of process (Fe^{3+}/Fe^{2+}) than the metal-ion/metal process (Ag^+/Ag). This is because the electron-transfer reactions are a more general and more important class of reactions than the more specific processes involved in the deposition or dissolution of a metal.

For both types of process the rate constants depend upon the potential difference at the interface. Let us see by how much the rate constant is altered if we change this potential difference by 1 V. From either eqn (1.10) or eqn (1.13)

$$k_1' = (k_1')_{\phi_M = \phi_S} \exp\left[-\frac{(1-\beta)F(\phi_M - \phi_S)}{RT}\right].$$

Taking

$$\beta = \tfrac{1}{2}, \qquad R = 8\ \mathrm{J\ mol^{-1}\ deg^{-1}},$$

$$T = 300\ \mathrm{K}, \qquad F = 10^5\ \mathrm{C\ mol^{-1}},$$

and

$$\phi_M - \phi_S = 1\ \mathrm{V},$$

then

$$\exp\left[-\frac{(1-\beta)F(\phi_M - \phi_S)}{RT}\right] \approx \exp\left[-\frac{\tfrac{1}{2}.10^5.1}{8.30}\right] \approx \exp(-20) \approx 10^{-9}.$$

Thus a change of 1 V alters the rate constant by a factor of 10^9.

Put in another way a change of only 118 mV changes the rate constant by a factor of 10.

This sensitivity of the rate constant to the potential arises from the exponential form of the law; it is similar to the sensitivity of rate constants to changes in temperature described by the Arrhenius equation. Thus with a twitch of his little finger the electrochemist can alter rate constants through many order of magnitude. In view of this almost divine power it is not surprising that the devotees of the cult have surrounded it with enough mumbo-jumbo to keep its arcane mysteries concealed from the eyes and understanding of lesser mortals.

12   Potential-dependent rate constants

Order of an electrochemical reaction

In homogeneous kinetics the order m of a reaction with respect to the species X is defined as

$$m_X = \left(\frac{\partial(\ln \text{rate})}{\partial(\ln [X])}\right)_{[Y] \text{ etc.}}$$

In electrochemical kinetics we take the same definition but because the rate is so sensitive to potential changes, we have to impose one further restriction: the potential at the electrode must remain constant. So for an electrochemical reaction

$$m_X = \left(\frac{\partial(\ln \text{rate})}{\partial(\ln [X]_0)}\right)_{(\phi_M - \phi_S), [Y] \text{ etc.}} \tag{1.18}$$

Tafel law

Imagine that we have the electrode at a potential where only one term in (1.16) is significant; for instance if it is so negative that the reaction

$$Fe^{3+} + e^- \rightarrow Fe^{2+}$$

takes place but the reverse reaction is negligible. Then

$$j = (k_1')_{\phi_M = \phi_S} [Fe^{3+}]_0 \exp\left[-\frac{\alpha F(\phi_M - \phi_S)}{RT}\right]$$

or in terms of current at the electrode of area A,

$$i = AF(k_1')_{\phi_M = \phi_S} [Fe^{3+}]_0 \exp\left[-\frac{\alpha F(\phi_M - \phi_S)}{RT}\right].$$

Taking logarithms of both sides we have:

$$\ln i = \text{constant} - \frac{\alpha F(\phi_M - \phi_S)}{RT}$$

$$= \text{another constant} - \frac{\alpha FE}{RT}. \tag{1.19}$$

where E is the observed potential across the electrochemical cell and we have assumed that any change in E produces the same change in $(\phi_M - \phi_S)$.

This is the *Tafel relation* which describes the effect of potential on the current. We shall postpone discussion of the relation in detail until Chapter 3. For the moment we will use (1.19) to define a general relationship for α. Since this is a general relation we will imagine a generalized electrochemical system

$$O + ne^- \rightarrow R,$$

and write

$$\alpha = -\frac{RT}{F}\left(\frac{\partial \ln i}{\partial E}\right)_{[O]_0} = -\frac{2.3RT}{F}\left(\frac{\partial \log i}{\partial E}\right)_{[O]_0}. \tag{1.20}$$

This equation applies to the reduction of a species O, when the reverse reaction is negligible. For the oxidation of a species R,

$$R \;\rightarrow\; O + ne^-,$$

we write

$$i = -AFk'_{-1}[R]_0 \exp\left(\frac{\beta F(\phi_M - \phi_S)}{RT}\right)$$

and

$$\beta = \frac{RT}{F}\left(\frac{\partial \ln(-i)}{\partial E}\right)_{[R]_0}. \tag{1.21}$$

In the simple one-electron transfers considered so far

$$\alpha + \beta = 1$$

but this is not necessarily true for multistep processes. Both α and β are experimental quantities and describe the gradients of the *Tafel plots* obtained by plotting log i against E. Their detailed interpretation remains for later.

Flux and current

In the equations in this chapter we have made considerable use of the flux j. This is because the flux j *is* the rate of the electrochemical reactions. In classical kinetics one has to measure the variation of concentration with time and plot a graph to obtain the rate of the reaction. The electrochemist merely has to measure a current and he has, with only one measurement, obtained a value for the rate of reaction. The relation between current and flux is

$$i = nFAj \tag{1.22}$$

where

j is the flux (mol m^{-2} s^{-1})
A is area of the electrode (m^2)
F is the Faraday (C mol^{-1})
n is the number of electrons per molecule reacting
and i is the current (C s^{-1}).

Traditionally electrochemists have expressed their rates in terms of current densities (i/A) such as standard exchange currents. However in order to use the same notation and concepts as ordinary kineticists in this book we will work with fluxes j and rate constants k'.

2. The distribution of potential

The measurement of $\phi_M - \phi_S$

HAVING emphasized the effect of the potential on the rate constants, and having described this with the term $\Delta\phi = (\phi_M - \phi_S)$ in (1.11) and (1.16), we have to admit first that there is no way of measuring this vital quantity, and secondly that the picture given in Chapter 1 is only a good first approximation, as it does not allow for the effects of the *double layer* that exists at the electrode–solution interface.

The question of the measurement of $\Delta\phi$ could well be taken over by the Zen Buddhists along with the question of the noise made by one hand clapping. Although we have so far concentrated our attention on an electrode process taking place at only one electrode, in fact to measure currents and potentials we have to have a complete electrical circuit. In such a circuit one cannot have only one interface between two dissimilar phases. The minimum number of interfaces is two. Hence there is no way of isolating the absolute potential difference at one interface. However one can design experimental conditions in such a way that the potential difference at all interfaces except one remains constant. One can then measure changes in $\phi_M - \phi_S$. Thus we can measure $\Delta(\phi_M - \phi_S)$ and investigate how a quantity X varies with changing $\phi_M - \phi_S$:

$$\frac{\partial X}{\partial(\phi_M - \phi_S)}.$$

This means that in Figs. 1.3 and 1.4 we cannot assign values to ϕ_S. For instance we cannot know the particular value of ϕ_S where the $G^\ominus$s of Fe^{2+} and Fe^{3+} are equal. But despite this the gradients of the lines OP, QR, and TS can be measured. The fact that numbers cannot be added to the scales in the figures does not affect the shapes of the surfaces.

Three electrodes rather than two

Classical electrochemical experiments are carried out in cells with two electrodes. For the study of electrode kinetics we in fact need three electrodes, as shown in Fig. 2.1. The *working electrode* is the electrode where the electrochemical reaction of interest is taking place. In order to measure changes in potential at that electrode we have a *reference electrode* through which no current flows. The condition of zero current ensures that the potential difference across the reference electrode–solution interface remains constant. (This hand when it claps at least makes a constant noise.) This electrode is very often a calomel electrode and is separated from the cell by a salt bridge with a sinter or with a capillary junction. Since no current is flowing no

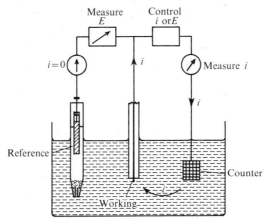

FIG. 2.1. Three electrodes are needed for studies of electrode kinetics rather than two. No current flows through reference electrode and hence E is not affected by potential drop at the counter-electrode.

harm arises from having a high resistance junction. The third electrode, the *counter electrode*, completes the circuit in the cell, and the current that passes through the working electrode passes through the counter electrode. However the potential difference needed to drive the current at the counter electrode is unimportant. If products from the reaction at the counter electrode interfere with the system then it too can be banished to the other side of a sinter.

The effect of iR drop

Since current is flowing in the cell between the working and the counter electrodes there is a further potential difference arising from the resistance of the electrolyte solution R_S. Hence neglecting any liquid junction potentials the measured potential difference is given by:

$$E = \Delta\phi_W - \Delta\phi_{Ref} + iR_S \tag{2.1}$$

where $\Delta\phi_W$ is the potential difference at the working electrode. Although we cannot experimentally separate E into $\Delta\phi_W$ and $\Delta\phi_{Ref}$ we can differentiate (2.1) with $\Delta\phi_{Ref}$ constant to give:

$$d\Delta\phi_W = dE(1 - R_S \, di/dE). \tag{2.2}$$

We now have to investigate the size of the quantity $R_S \, di/dE$. If this quantity is large compared to 1 then the major changes in the potential difference will be across the bulk of the solution; if it is small compared to 1 then the changes in potential will take place at the electrode–solution interface. Since we are interested in the measurement of electrode kinetics, rather than the conductivity of electrolyte solutions, we wish to eliminate the first possibility, and so choose experimental conditions where

$$R_S \, di/dE \ll 1,$$

and

$$d\Delta\phi_W \approx dE. \tag{2.3}$$

The value of R_S depends upon the salt concentration in the solution. For [Salt] $= 10^3 \text{ mol m}^{-3}$ typical values give an estimate of $R_S \, di/dE \sim 0.01$. However for [Salt] $= 1 \text{ mol m}^{-3}$,

$$R_S \, di/dE \sim 10.$$

Hence to be able to neglect the iR drop in the bulk of the solution one adds a large concentration ($\sim 10^3 \text{ mol m}^{-3} = 1 \text{ M}$) of inert electrolyte, for example KCl or NaClO$_4$ to carry the current in the liquid phase. In ordinary solution kinetics and thermodynamics, experiments are carried out as far as possible at 'infinite dilution'. To study electrode kinetics one has to abandon the perfection of infinite dilution in favour of a solution that will carry the current. For systems which have fast electrode kinetics, for large concentrations of reactants, or for work in non-aqueous solvents, where the conductivity of electrolytes may be smaller or it may be difficult to achieve [Salt] $\sim 10^3 \text{ mol m}^{-3}$ one may not be able to set up experimental conditions with

$$R_S \, di/dE \ll 1.$$

So instead of (2.2) one has to correct the measured values of E for the iR drop and work with

$$d\Delta\phi_W = dE'$$

where

$$E' = E - iR_S.$$

The ideal polarized electrode

But even though from either (2.2) or (2.3) we can measure changes in $\Delta\phi_W$, unfortunately the potential difference at the interface is not all available to drive the electrode reaction, because of the distribution of potential in the solution close to the electrode. To discuss this we consider an inert electrode at which electrochemical reactions do *not* take place. We take an example, described by Grahame, of a mercury electrode in a 1 M solution of KCl; the potential is measured with respect to a calomel electrode:

$$\text{Hg} \big| \text{Hg}_2 \text{Cl}_2 \text{(s) KCl aq (1M)} \big| \text{KCl aq (1M)} \big| \text{Hg} \quad \text{—E}$$

Reference electrode   Working electrode

The left hand electrode is a reversible system and the overall electrochemical equilibrium

$$e^- + \tfrac{1}{2}Hg_2Cl_2 \rightleftarrows Hg + Cl^-$$

is a labile one.

On the other hand at the right hand electrode, where there is no $HgCl_2$, over a wide potential range no electrochemical reactions are possible. For instance Grahame calculated the following equilibrium concentrations for the products of possible reactions when $E = -0.556$ V:

Reaction	Equilibrium concentration
$Hg \rightarrow \tfrac{1}{2}Hg_2^{2+} + e^-$	$[Hg_2^{2+}] = 10^{-33}$ mol m^{-3}
$K_s^+ + e^- \rightarrow K$ (in Hg)	$x_K = 10^{-45}$ (in Hg)
$Cl^- \rightarrow \tfrac{1}{2}Cl_2 + e^-$	$p_{Cl_2} = 10^{-28}$ atm
$H_2O + e^- \rightarrow \tfrac{1}{2}H_2 + OH$	$p_{H_2} = 4 \times 10^{-3}$ atm.

The only reaction which on thermodynamic grounds could produce any significant quantity of product is the decomposition of the solvent H_2O; however the kinetic barrier to the production of H_2 on a Hg surface is large and this reaction is prevented by its large activation energy. This type of electrode where, as Grahame says, 'each charged particle stays on its own side of the fence', is termed an *'ideal polarized electrode'*.

Breakdown of electroneutrality

What happens when we apply different potentials E to the system? There can be no continuous passage of direct current through the system because no charge is transferred across the right hand interface. However, if E is sufficiently negative the K^+ ions will be attracted towards the working electrode and the Cl^- ions will be repelled (if E is sufficiently positive the reverse will happen). Hence although in the bulk of the solution $[K^+] = [Cl^-]$, near the electrode this condition does not hold; depending on E there will be an excess of either K^+ or Cl^-.

Now we can ask two related questions: first what is the variation of the potential with distance near the electrode and secondly what is the distribution of the ions near the electrode? The answers to these questions will be important to our understanding of electrode kinetics for two reasons. First, while, as described in Chapter 1, the reaction rates are sensitive to changes in potential, the only changes which affect the actual electrode processes are those at the electrode–solution interface itself. Secondly, the rates will be dependent on the numbers of ions next to the electrode, and these numbers will be changed if ions are attracted or repelled by the electrode. Two models have been suggested, the Helmholtz model and the Gouy–Chapman model. These two were combined by Stern and this combination is supported by the experimental evidence. But we first consider each model in turn.

Helmholtz model

In 1879 Helmholtz proposed the simplest model. This was that the ions attracted towards the electrode were lined up in the solution a fixed distance away from the electrode. Their charge is balanced by an equal number of electrons near the surface of the metal. Remember that the charges cannot neutralize each other because they are constrained to stay on their 'own side of the fence'. The whole arrangement is like a parallel-plate condenser and is drawn in Fig. 2.2. The positive ions drawn in the diagram are not all the K^+ in the vicinity of the electrode but are the excess ions over and above the Cl^- which remains at the electrode,

$$\oplus = [K^+]_0 - [Cl^-]_0.$$

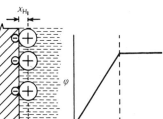
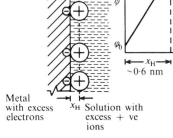

FIG. 2.2. Helmholtz model of double layer showing excess +ve ions being attracted to a negatively charged electrode, and the variation of potential with distance from the electrode.

This separation of charge is the reason for the name *double layer*, which is now used to describe the whole region close to the electrode where the condition of electroneutrality breaks down. The distance x_H in Fig. 2.2 is governed by the hydration spheres of the ions. It is called the *outer Helmholtz plane*. The whole potential difference is concentrated across a distance of about 1 nm and this leads for potential differences of 0.1 to 1 V to fields of 10^8 to 10^9 V m^{-1}.

Fields as large as this orient the water molecules. Hence this orientation, as shown in Fig. 2.3, will complicate the distribution of potential and will mean that the dielectric constant of the solvent in this first layer is less than that in the bulk of the solution. To a first approximation we assume that the Helmholtz model is like a parallel-plate condenser and has a constant capacity per unit area which we can write

$$C'_H = \frac{\varepsilon}{x_H} = \frac{K_\varepsilon \varepsilon_0}{x_H} \tag{2.4}$$

where C'_H is in units of $F\ m^{-2}$, x_H is the distance to the outer Helmholtz plane (in m), ε_0 is the permittivity of a vacuum, and K_ε is the relative permittivity (it used to be the dielectric constant). With typical values of $K_\varepsilon \approx 7$ (less than the bulk value because of the high field) and $x_H = 0.6\ nm$ (6 Å):

$$C'_H \approx 0.1\ F\ m^{-2} = 10\mu F\ cm^{-2}. \tag{2.5}$$

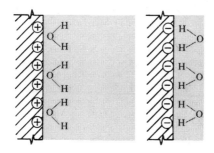

FIG. 2.3. Orientation of water layer next to the electrode for an anode and a cathode. This orientation is one of the reasons why $\phi_M \neq \phi_0$; there is an unknown potential drop at the interface.

Gouy–Chapman model

In this model the excess ions are released from standing to attention next to the electrode and as a result of the thermal motions they roam about in the region of the electrode. Their distribution is then a balance between the ordering forces of the electric field and the disorder caused by thermal motion. This balance is exactly the same as that in the Debye–Hückel theory. However Gouy and Chapman independently proposed the model in 1910, more than a decade before the Debye–Hückel theory (1923).

Distribution of potential

In the Debye–Hückel theory† one calculates the variation of potential and distribution of ions around a central ion; this means that the solution

† See Chapter 1 of Robbins, *loc. cit.*

has spherical symmetry. For the 'diffuse double layer' or the ionic atmosphere of an electrode one assumes that the electrode is a plane and calculates the variation of potential and distribution of ions in the direction (x) perpendicular to the electrode, as shown in Fig. 2.4. As before,

$$\ominus = [Cl^-] - [K^+].$$

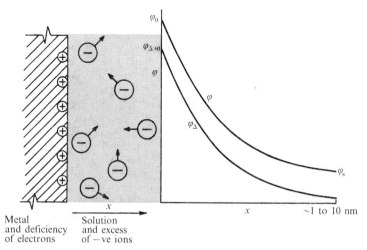

FIG. 2.4. Gouy–Chapman model of diffuse double layer showing $-$ve ions being attracted to a positively charged electrode. The variation of potential is also shown plotted both as ϕ and as ϕ_Δ where $\phi_\Delta = \phi - \phi_S$.

We now write

$$\phi_\Delta = \phi - \phi_S,$$

so that ϕ_Δ describes the change in potential at the electrode and it goes to zero in the bulk of the solution. The calculation is carried out in terms of ϕ_Δ.

Poisson–Boltzmann equation

The Poisson equation, which relates the potential to the charge distribution generating it is:

$$\frac{\partial^2 \phi_\Delta(x)}{\partial x^2} = \frac{-\rho(x)}{\varepsilon}. \tag{2.6}$$

The potential varies only in the x-direction hence the derivatives with respect to y and z parallel to the plane of the electrode, disappear. The charge at x

is given by

$$\rho(x) = \sum_i z_i e N_i(x). \tag{2.7}$$

where the ith ion has a charge $z_i e$, and $N_i(x)$ describes its distribution function in number of ions per unit volume. We assume that the distribution function obeys the Boltzmann distribution law† and

$$N_i(x) = N_i(\infty) \exp\left[-\frac{z_i e \phi_\Delta(x)}{k_B T}\right]. \tag{2.8}$$

From (2.6) to (2.8) we obtain the form of the Poisson–Boltzmann equation for this problem:‡

$$\frac{\partial^2 \phi_\Delta}{\partial x^2} = -\frac{1}{\varepsilon} \sum_i z_i e N_i(\infty) \exp\left[-\frac{z_i e \phi_\Delta}{k_B T}\right]. \tag{2.9}$$

This equation has to be solved with the boundary conditions

$$\text{at} \quad x = 0 \qquad \phi_\Delta = \phi_{\Delta,0}$$

and

$$\text{as} \quad x \to \infty \qquad \phi_\Delta \to 0.$$

In the Debye–Hückel theory the exponential term in (2.8) is expanded and the theory therefore only holds for

$$\left(\frac{e\phi}{k_B T}\right)^2 \ll 1.$$

In the double layer because of the applied potentials we cannot make this approximation so we retain the full exponential form of the Boltzmann Distribution Law. To obtain simple analytical solutions we do however restrict ourselves to the case where, in the Σ in (2.9), the major contribution comes from the cation and anion of a symmetrical (z, z)-electrolyte. We can accept this restriction since we shall then have a theory for studies involving binary electrolytes and for the more common type of experiment in which there is a large concentration of inert electrolyte (e.g. KCl or $NaClO_4$).

---

† Derived in Gasser and Richards, *Entropy and energy levels* (OCS 19).
‡ It has been claimed that (2.9) is fundamentally unsound since it violates the 'principle of the linear superposition of fields'. This principle states that if, for a system of fixed charges, all the charges are doubled then the potential will also be doubled. However the system studied here is not a system of fixed charges and if the charges on the ions were doubled then one would indeed obtain a different distribution function. Hence the principle is irrelevant to the problem under consideration.

Therefore for a (z, z)-electrolyte,

$$\frac{d^2\phi_\Delta}{dx^2} = -\frac{zeN_\infty}{\varepsilon}\left[\exp\left(-\frac{ze\phi_\Delta}{k_BT}\right) - \exp\left(\frac{ze\phi_\Delta}{k_BT}\right)\right]$$

$$= \frac{2zeN_\infty}{\varepsilon}\sinh\left(\frac{ze\phi_{\Delta'}}{k_BT}\right).$$

To avoid cluttering up the pages with symbols we will now express this equation in dimensionless variables. Writing

$$\theta = \frac{ze\phi_\Delta}{2k_BT}$$

and

$$\chi = x/x_{DL},$$

where

$$x_{DL} = \frac{1}{ze}\sqrt{\left(\frac{\varepsilon k_BT}{2N_\infty}\right)},$$

we obtain

$$\frac{d^2\theta}{d\chi^2} = \tfrac{1}{2}\sinh(2\theta). \tag{2.10}$$

The Debye length

The distance x_{DL} is the same as the Debye length in the Debye–Hückel theory, when the Debye length is worked out for a (z, z) electrolyte. To evaluate it from experimental quantities we write

$$x_{DL} = \frac{1}{ze}\sqrt{\left(\frac{\varepsilon k_BT}{2N_\infty}\right)} = \frac{1}{zF}\sqrt{\left(\frac{\varepsilon_0 K_\varepsilon RT}{2c_\infty}\right)}. \tag{2.11}$$

Evaluation of the constants gives

$$x_{DL} = \frac{6\cdot3\times10^{-11}}{z}\sqrt{\left(\frac{K_\varepsilon T}{c_\infty}\right)}$$

where x_{DL} is in m, c_∞ is in mol m^{-3} or mM, and K_ε is the ratio of permittivities (dielectric constant). Fig. 2.5 shows how x_{DL} varies with c_∞ for $z = 1$, $K = 78$ and $T = 298$ K; for these values

$$x_{DL} = 9\cdot6\times10^{-9}\, c_\infty^{-\frac{1}{2}}.$$

Also x_{DL} increases with $T^{\frac{1}{2}}$, that is the breakdown of the condition of electroneutrality spreads further out from the electrode the larger is the thermal energy.

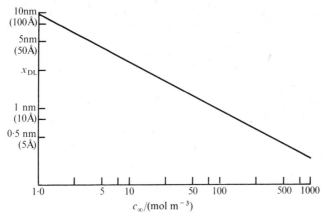

FIG. 2.5. Variation of the Debye length with concentration of a $(1, 1)$ electrolyte in water at 298 K. Note the log scales.

Solution of the Poisson–Boltzmann equation

We therefore have to solve the differential equation,

$$\frac{\partial^2 \theta}{\partial \chi^2} = \tfrac{1}{2}\sinh{(2\theta)},$$

with the two boundary conditions, (1) next to the electrode $\chi = 0$ and $\theta = \theta_0$, and (2) far away from the electrode, $\chi \to \infty$ and $\theta \to 0$. The solution of this equation is given in Appendix (1). It is not difficult and in many ways is easier than the corresponding problem in the Debye–Hückel theory since one does not have to write pages justifying dubious approximations. The answer is

$$\tanh{(\tfrac{1}{2}\theta)} = \tanh{(\tfrac{1}{2}\theta_0)} \exp{(-\chi)}. \tag{2.12}$$

The function $\tanh{(\lambda)}$ is

$$\tanh{(\lambda)} = \frac{\exp{(\lambda)} - \exp{(-\lambda)}}{\exp{(\lambda)} + \exp{(-\lambda)}}.$$

This function comes in to our equations so much that it is plotted in Fig. 2.6 so that you can see its shape.

Comparison with Debye–Hückel theory

It is interesting to compare this result with that from the Debye–Hückel theory:

$$\phi_\Lambda(r) = \frac{z_i e}{4\pi\varepsilon(1 + a/x_{DL})} \frac{\exp{(a/x_{DL})}}{r \exp{(r/x_{DL})}}, \dagger$$

† See Robbins, *Ions in solution 2. An introduction to electrochemistry* (OCS 2) p.6.

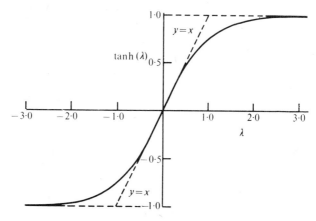

FIG. 2.6. Plot of tanh (λ) against λ. Note that for small values of λ, tanh $(\lambda) \simeq \lambda$, and for large values of $|\lambda|$, tanh $(\lambda) \approx \pm 1$.

where a is the radius of the ion. We replace r by $a+x$ and we write $\phi_{\Delta,0}$ for the potential when $r = a$ or $x = 0$; then

$$\frac{\phi_{\Delta}}{\phi_{\Delta,0}} = \frac{a}{a+x}\exp\left(-\frac{x}{x_{DL}}\right).$$

We now allow the central test ion to swell to an enormous size so that it becomes locally flat and resembles the electrode; that is we allow a to become very large. Then

$$\frac{\phi_{\Delta}}{\phi_{\Delta,0}} = \exp(-\chi). \tag{2.13}$$

The Debye–Hückel theory is derived with the assumption that $\theta^2 \ll 1$, and applying this condition to (2.17),

$$\frac{\tanh(\frac{1}{2}\theta)}{\tanh(\frac{1}{2}\theta_0)} \simeq \frac{\theta}{\theta_0} = \frac{\phi_{\Delta}}{\phi_{\Delta,0}} = \exp(-\chi). \tag{2.14}$$

Eqns (2.13) and (2.14) are identical and we obtain the same result by the two different methods. However (2.12) is more useful to use since here we have not assumed that θ has to be small.

This comparison emphasises the similarity between the ionic atmosphere of an ion and the diffuse double layer of an electrode. Although fanciful, it is instructive sometimes to consider an electrode as a single giant molecule whose reactivity and charge can be changed by the electrochemist. In this case we are considering changes in charge. In the case of the electrode it is easy to see that the distribution of ions near the electrode will be affected by the charge on the electrode and that there will be an excess of positive ions if the electrode is negatively charged and vice versa. In the Debye–Hückel theory the distinction between the electrode and the surrounding ions is lost and we have to select one ion to play the part of the electrode and to consider the distribution of ions around that particular test ion. For the electrode we can assume that the surface is flat while for the test ion we have to work in spherical co-ordinates. The mathematics for the flat surface does not involve so many approximations and the equations can be solved without having to assume that the field produces only a small perturbation on the concentration.

Distribution of potential in the diffuse layer

Fig. 2.7 shows plots of θ against χ for different values of θ_0. Remember that θ describes the potential difference in the double layer. When $\theta \sim \frac{1}{2}$ the thermal energy and the energy of interaction between the ion and the field of the electrode are about equal. The distance is described by χ in terms of multiples of the Debye length. From Fig. 2.7 we see that θ decays to zero

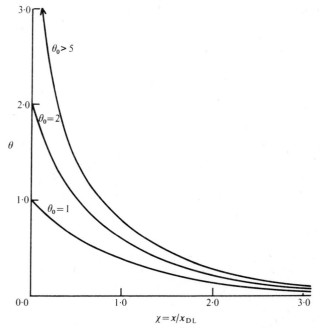

Fig. 2.7. Plots of eqn. (2.12) showing variation of potential with distance in the diffuse double layer. Below $\theta = 1$, $\tanh(\frac{1}{2}\theta) \approx \frac{1}{2}\theta$ (see Fig. 2.6) and θ decays exponentially with distance. For $\theta_0 > 5$, $\tanh(\frac{1}{2}\theta_0) \approx 1$ and a limiting curve is found.

when $\chi \sim 3$. This means that the strong field of the electrode is contained within a distance of at most $3x_{DL}$ of the electrode where typical values of x_{DL} are shown in Fig. 2.5.

We have now answered the first question we asked about the distribution of potential near the electrode. We have still got to find what effect this potential has on the concentrations of the ions.

Distribution of ions in the diffuse layer

From the Boltzmann Distribution Law, (2.8), the variation in concentration of the ions near the electrode is given by

$$\frac{c}{c_\infty} = \exp\left(\pm\frac{ze\phi_\Delta}{k_B T}\right) = \exp\left(\pm 2\theta\right).$$

Now

$$\exp\left(-\theta\right) = \frac{1-\tanh\left(\frac{1}{2}\theta\right)}{1+\tanh\left(\frac{1}{2}\theta\right)}.$$

We then substitute from (2.12) and taking θ positive so that $\exp\left(-2\theta\right)$ describes the concentration of the cation that is repelled from the electrode, we obtain:

$$\frac{c_{repelled}}{c_\infty} = \tanh^2\left\{\frac{1}{2}[\chi + f(\theta_0)]\right\} \tag{2.15}$$

where

$$f(\theta_0) = -\ln\left[\tanh\left(\frac{1}{2}\theta_0\right)\right]. \tag{2.16}$$

For the anion which is attracted to the electrode:

$$\frac{c_{attracted}}{c_\infty} = \coth^2\left\{\frac{1}{2}[\chi + f(\theta_0)]\right\}. \tag{2.17}$$

If θ is negative then (2.15) applies to the repelled anion and (2.17) to the attracted cation, and

$$f(\theta_0) = -\ln\left[\tanh\left(-\frac{1}{2}\theta_0\right)\right].$$

The breakdown of the condition of electroneutrality is shown in Fig. 2.8 by plotting (2.15) and (2.17) for different values of θ_0. As with the potential, for $\chi > 5$ the condition of electroneutrality is restored. Hence the DL in x_{DL} can also stand for 'diffuse layer', for it measures the thickness of the layer in which there are large potential gradients and in which there are not equal numbers of cations and anions.

In Fig. 2.8 we can see that even quite small values of θ_0 will alter the concentrations significantly. For instance for $\theta_0 \approx \frac{1}{2}$ corresponding to a potential difference of only $50\,mV$ the concentrations are altered by a factor of 3. For larger values of θ_0 the concentration of the repelled ion approaches zero

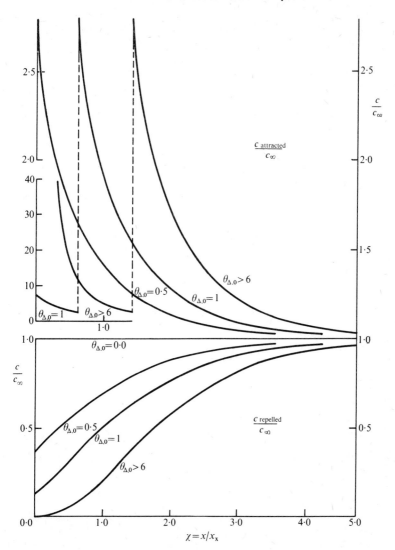

Fig. 2.8. Breakdown of the condition of electroneutrality for a (z, z) electrolyte according to (2.14) and (2.17) for different values of $\theta_{\Delta,0}$, the potential difference across the diffuse double layer.

and this makes it difficult for it to react on the electrode. On the other hand the concentration of the attracted ion is many times its value in the bulk of the solution.

Capacitance of diffuse layer

Having described the Helmholtz and Gouy–Chapman models we now have to follow Stern and consider a combination of both models in order to answer the question whether the potential change will be concentrated across the very small distance x_H (the hydration sphere) as shown in Fig. 2.2 or whether it will spread out into the solution for several multiples of the Debye length as shown in Fig. 2.7. In the first case all the potential difference will be available to drive the electrode reaction; in the second case only some fraction of it will be available at the actual electrode solution interface. To answer this important question we consider the region near the electrode to consist of two capacitances in series but first we need to calculate the capacitance of the diffuse double layer.

Even though the build up of charge is spread over a distance of $x \sim x_{DL}$, rather than at a plane as in the Helmholtz model, there will still be a balancing charge on the electrode and the assembly of charges will again act as a capacitance. To calculate the capacitance we write for ρ the charge per unit volume

$$\rho = zF[c_\infty \exp(-2\theta) - c_\infty \exp(2\theta)]$$

$$= -2zFc_\infty \sinh(2\theta).$$

The total charge q per unit area is then obtained by integrating ρ from the electrode out into the bulk of the solution:

$$q = \int_0^\infty \rho \, dx = -x_{DL} 2zFc_\infty \int_0^\infty \sinh(2\theta) \, d\chi$$

$$= -4\chi_{DL} zFc_\infty \sinh\theta_0.$$

The integral is worked out in Appendix 1. The minus sign arises since a positive value of θ_0 will attract negative ions. Substitution from (2.11) for x_{DL} then gives

$$q = -8\varepsilon_0 K_\varepsilon RTc_\infty \sinh\frac{ze\phi_{\Delta,0}}{2k_B T}. \tag{2.18}$$

Note that $q = 0$ when $\phi_{\Delta,0} = 0$. The potential where the capacitor is uncharged is called the *potential of zero charge*.

We can now work out C'_{DL}, the capacity per unit area of the diffuse layer, by differentiating (2.18)

$$C'_{DL} = -\frac{dq}{d\phi_{\Delta,0}} = zF \sqrt{\left(\frac{2\varepsilon_0 K_\varepsilon c_\infty}{RT}\right)} \cosh\left(\frac{ze\phi_{\Delta,0}}{2k_B T}\right). \tag{2.19}$$

Let us write

$$C'_{DL,0} = zF\sqrt{\left(\frac{2\varepsilon_0 K_\varepsilon c_\infty}{RT}\right)} = 0.141z\sqrt{\left(\frac{K_\varepsilon c_\infty}{T}\right)}, \qquad (2.20)$$

and for $z = 1$, $K_\varepsilon = 78$ and $T = 298$ K

$$C'_{DL,0} = 0.072c_\infty^{\frac{1}{2}},$$

where

$$c_\infty \text{ is in mol m}^{-3} \text{ or mM}$$

and

$$C'_{DL,0} \text{ is in F m}^{-2} \text{ or } (\mu\text{F mm}^{-2}).$$

Fig. 2.9 shows how $C'_{DL,0}$ varies with the concentration of the electrolyte. Also shown is the value of C'_H the capacity of the Helmholtz model that we calculated in (2.5). Eqn (2.19) now becomes

$$C'_{DL} = C'_{DL,0} \cosh(\theta_0).$$

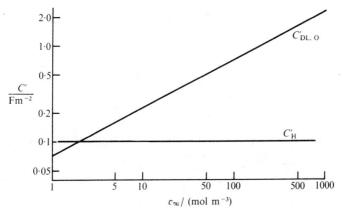

FIG. 2.9. Variation of differential capacities per unit area with the concentration of electrolyte.

Unlike ordinary capacitors, C'_{DL} is not constant with θ the variable describing potential. On the contrary the $\cosh(\theta_0)$ term can cause very large variations. It is plotted in Fig. 2.10.

The combined model of the double layer

Stern combined both the models we have discussed into a picture of the double layer in which, next to the electrode, we have the region of high field

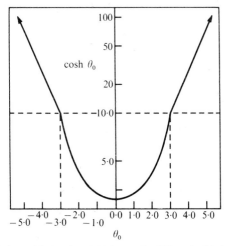

FIG. 2.10. Variation with θ_0 of cosh (θ_0) term in diffuse double layer capacitance. Note that the y scale becomes logarithmic for $y > 10$ and that cosh $(0) = 1$.

and low dielectric constant with a row of firmly held ions; beyond that there is the ionic atmosphere of the electrode or the diffuse layer where there is a balance between the electrostatic forces and the random thermal motions. Fig. 2.11 shows a schematic diagram of the extra ions around the electrode. The variation of potential is also sketched. It falls linearly across the Helmholtz part of the double layer and then decays away to zero according to (2.12) across the diffuse part; the distance x in the diffuse part and χ are measured from the Helmholtz plane and $\phi_{\Delta,0}$ is replaced by $\phi_{\Delta,H}$. The boundary between the two parts is called the *outer Helmholtz plane*. The corresponding difference in the description of ions in solution is the difference between an ion pair and an ionic atmosphere.

Now we can answer the question as to which is the more important—the Helmholtz layer or the diffuse layer? The model can be analysed into two capacitances connected in series:

$$\text{Electrode} \underset{C'_H}{\overset{\varphi_0 \quad \varphi_H}{-\vdash\vdash-}} \underset{C'_{DL}}{\overset{\varphi_S}{-\vdash\vdash-}} \text{Solution}$$

For such an arrangement the overall capacitance is given by:

$$\frac{1}{C'_\Sigma} = \frac{1}{C'_H} + \frac{1}{C'_{DL}}. \tag{2.21}$$

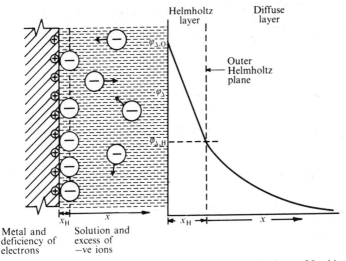

Helmholtz layer   Diffuse layer

Outer Helmholtz plane

Metal and deficiency of electrons

Solution and excess of −ve ions

FIG. 2.11. Combined model of double layer showing a Helmholtz layer of fixed ions and a diffuse layer containing mobile ions. Variation of potential (ϕ_Δ) is also shown.

This equation tells us that the *smaller* of the two capacitances determines the overall capacitance. If C'_H and C'_{DL} are of very different size then the term containing the *larger* one can be neglected in (2.21). We can express this pictorially by writing the two extreme cases in Table 2.1.

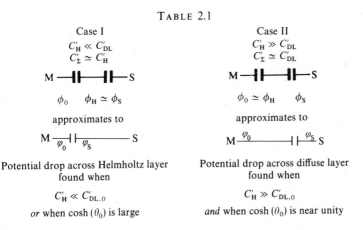

TABLE 2.1

Case I	Case II
$C'_H \ll C'_{DL}$	$C'_H \gg C'_{DL}$
$C'_\Sigma \simeq C'_H$	$C'_\Sigma \simeq C'_{DL}$
M ⊣⊢ ⊣⊢ S	M ⊣⊢ ⊣⊢ S
$\phi_0 \quad \phi_H \simeq \phi_S$	$\phi_0 \simeq \phi_H \quad \phi_S$
approximates to	approximates to
M $\overset{\phi_0}{\dashv}$⊦ ϕ_S S	M $\overset{\phi_0}{\rule{2cm}{0.4pt}}$ ⊦ ϕ_S S
Potential drop across Helmholtz layer found when	Potential drop across diffuse layer found when
$C'_H \ll C'_{DL,0}$	$C'_H \gg C'_{DL,0}$
or when $\cosh(\theta_0)$ is large	*and* when $\cosh(\theta_0)$ is near unity

We have also summarized the conditions under which both situations will be found. Note that for case II not only has C'_H got to be greater than $C'_{DL,0}$ but also the cosh (θ_0) term must not have blown up. Figs. 2.9 and 2.10 respectively compare C'_H and $C'_{DL,0}$ and show the cosh (θ_0) function.

We shall now see if this theoretical model is supported by experiment.

Electro-capillary experiments

A simple type of experiment using a mercury electrode in a capillary allows one to investigate the properties of the double layer. A simplified form of the apparatus is shown in Fig. 2.12. No current flows through the cell since no reactions can take place at the interface. The experiment consists of setting a potential on the potentiometer and then adjusting h, the height of the mercury column, so that the mercury water interface remains in the same position. In this way one measures the surface tension at the interface as a function of the potential applied by the potentiometer. The mass of the

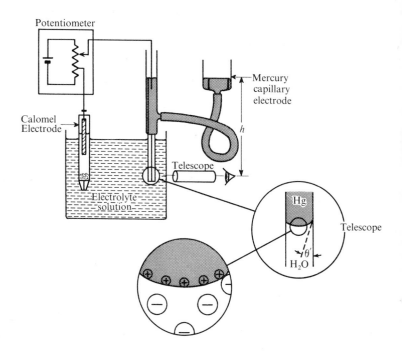

FIG. 2.12. Electrocapillary experiment. At each potential h is adjusted so that the meniscus remains in the same place. Magnified insets show the contact angle θ' and the charges repelling each other at the interface.

mercury column is balanced by the surface tension and

$$2\pi r \quad \times \quad \gamma \quad \times \quad \cos\theta' \quad = \quad \pi r^2 h \quad \times \quad \rho_{Hg} \quad \times \quad g$$

Circum-ference	Surface tension	Contact angle	Volume of Hg	Density of Hg	Gravitational constant

Hence γ can be found from measurements of h.

The Lippmann equation

The Lippmann equation describes how the surface tension of the mercury water interface is affected by the charge on the interface. The more highly charged the curved interface becomes the more the charges repel each other, thereby decreasing the cohesive forces and lowering the surface tension. This is sketched schematically in Fig. 2.12. The Lippmann equation states

$$\left(\frac{\partial\gamma}{\partial\Delta\phi}\right)_{T,A_H,\mu_i \text{ etc}} = -\frac{Q_M}{A}, \tag{2.22}$$

where

A_H is the Helmholtz free energy

Q_M is the total charge on the metal

A is the area of the interface

and

$$\Delta\phi = \phi_M - \phi_S.$$

The change in surface tension is equal to the charge per unit area multiplied by the change in potential. The equation is derived in Appendix (2).

Now

$$d(\Delta\phi) \simeq d(\phi_{\Delta,0}),$$

and since the charges on the metal and in the solution are equal and opposite

$$\frac{Q_M}{A} = q_M = -q_S.$$

So we may write,

$$\left(\frac{\partial\gamma}{\partial\phi_{\Delta,0}}\right)_{T,\text{ etc}} = q_S. \tag{2.23}$$

Now if we take the simplest case of a constant double-layer capacitance which does not vary with potential, then

$$q_S = -C'_\Sigma \phi_{\Delta,0}.$$

Substitution in and integration of (2.23) gives

$$\gamma = \gamma_{max} - \tfrac{1}{2}C'_{\Sigma}(\phi_{\Delta,0})^2. \qquad (2.24)$$

This equation describes a parabolic dependence of γ on $\phi_{\Delta,0}$ as shown in Fig. 2.13. The maximum value of γ is found when

$$\phi_{\Delta,0} = 0 \quad \text{or} \quad q_S = 0.$$

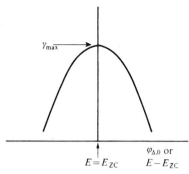

FIG. 2.13. Plot of (2.24) showing predicted variation of surface tension with applied potential for a constant double layer capacitance.

This is again the *potential of zero charge* where the double layer capacitance is uncharged. The surface tension is a maximum because on the uncharged surface there is no repulsion between the like charges. On the laboratory scale we will call this point E_{zc}. It might be thought that at this point $\Delta\phi = 0$ and $\phi_M = \phi_S$. If this was so, then we would be able to know the potential difference across a single interface. However there will still be an unknown degree of orientation of the water dipoles at the interface (see Fig. 2.3). This orientation means that there is also a potential drop across this dipole layer. This will be present even when there are no ions in the solution. So although $\phi_{\Delta,0} = 0$ and $\phi_0 = \phi_S$ we cannot conclude that $\phi_M = \phi_0$ nor that $\phi_M = \phi_S$ at the potential of zero charge. However the potential of zero charge does provide a good reference potential for double layer studies; also it does relate the ϕ_Δ scale used so far in the discussion to the practical values measured in the laboratory:

$$\phi_0 = \phi_S \quad \text{and} \quad \phi_{\Delta,0} = 0, \quad \text{when } E = E_{zc}.$$

Experimental results

Fig. 2.14 shows some real experimental electrocapillary curves. To a first approximation they do indeed have a parabolic shape. In order to obtain the

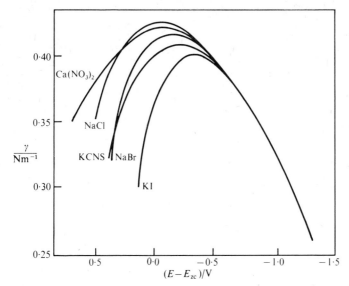

FIG. 2.14. Typical electro-capillary curves showing variation of γ with applied potential. Data from Grahame, *Chem. Rev.*, 1947, **41**, 441.

parabola we integrated (2.23) assuming C'_Σ constant. In practice one goes in the opposite direction. From the variation of the surface tension γ with the observed e.m.f. E, and assuming

$$dE = d(\phi_{\Delta,0})$$

we can see from (2.23) that the gradient of the experimental curve is a direct measurement of the total charge per unit area on the electrode. By differentiating (2.23) we obtain

$$\frac{d^2\gamma}{dE^2} = \frac{dq}{d\phi_{\Delta,0}} = -C'_\Sigma. \tag{2.25}$$

Thus the second differential of the electrocapillary curve gives directly the differential capacity of the double layer. Fig. 2.15 shows this procedure for the case of the parabola. Results for the differential capacity obtained from analysis of the electrocapillary curves can be compared with measurements of the capacitance using an a.c. bridge and with results from a direct method in which the flow of charge carried by falling mercury drops of known surface area was measured. Fig. 2.16 is a comparison by Grahame of the three

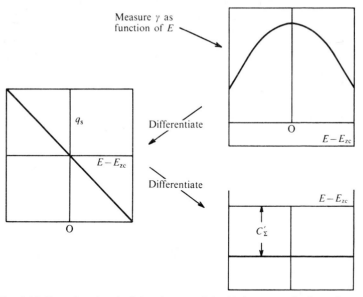

FIG. 2.15. Procedure for obtaining charge and double layer capacity from electrocapillary curve. Example shown has a constant value of C'_Σ: this is not found in practice but procedure will still work.

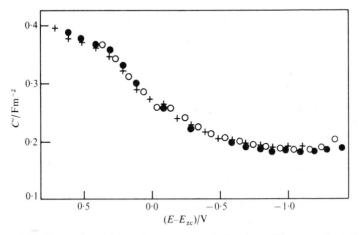

FIG. 2.16. Comparison of capacity measurements by three different methods for $500 \text{ mol m}^{-3} \text{ Na}_2\text{SO}_4$; electrocapillary curves, $+$; a.c. capacitance measurements, $\bullet$; direct method of measuring charge on falling Hg drops, $\circ$. (Taken from Grahame, *Chem. Rev.*, 1947, **41**, 441.)

methods and it can be seen that results from the three very different types of experiment are in good agreement.

Fig. 2.17 shows Grahame's results for the differential capacity of a mercury drop electrode for different concentrations of NaF. For an electrolyte concentration of 1 mol dm^{-3} we find from Fig. 2.9 that $C'_{DL,0} \gg C'_H$. Hence we have case I of Table 2.1; the capacitance of the diffuse double layer does not contribute much to the observed capacitance and $C' \simeq C'_H$. According to the simplest Helmholtz model C'_H should be constant; this is found to be only a rough approximation. As the concentration decreases a more and more pronounced minimum occurs in the curves. This minimum is centred around the potential of zero charge. It is the effect of the diffuse double layer. As discussed above, in case II of Table 2.1 when $C'_H \simeq C'_{DL,0}$, the contribution from C'_{DL} will decrease C'_Σ near the potential of zero charge where $\cosh \theta_0 \simeq 1$, but will be negligible at larger values of $|\theta_0|$. Thus the sharp minimum is caused by the $\cosh \theta_0$ term (see Fig. 2.10) swinging C'_Σ from case I to case II for $\theta_0 \sim 0$ and back to case I. These sharp minima at the potential of zero charge are generally seen when $c_\infty \sim 1$ mol m^{-3} or 1 mM.

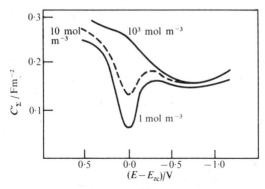

FIG. 2.17. Variation of differential capacity with applied potential and concentration for NaF at a Hg electrode. Note at low concentrations the sharp minimum around the potential of zero charge caused by the diffuse double layer. Data from Grahame, *J. Am. chem. Soc.*, 1954, **76**, 4819.

One can take the C'_H measured in 1 mol dm^{-3} NaF and combine it with the C'_{DL} from the Gouy–Chapman theory to calculate C'_Σ. Fig. 2.18 shows such a comparison for $c_\infty = 1$ mol m^{-3}. The agreement is reasonable especially since we have had to assume that C'_H is unchanged from 1 mol dm^{-3} or 1 mol m^{-3}. Thus our model of the double layer with its separation into two terms agrees reasonably well with experiment. The diffuse layer model is particularly successful in describing the appearance of the sharp minima at low concentration. Since the arguments are so similar this agreement supports

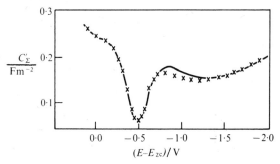

FIG. 2.18. Comparison of theoretical and experimental capacitance for 1 mol m^{-3} NaF. Measured values of C'_H at 10^3 mol m^{-3} are combined with theory for C'_{DL} to predict the curve at 1 mol m^{-3}. (Data from Grahame.)

the Debye–Hückel theory of electrolytes. It is perhaps easier to think of the ionic atmosphere of the electrode than to think of the mutual effects of different ions on each other. The capacitance experiments in dilute solutions are direct evidence for the real existence of ionic atmospheres.

Distribution of potential and electrolyte concentration

From the arguments so far we see that the distribution of potential between two electrodes is sensitive to the concentration of electrolyte. Three cases are shown in Fig. 2.19. Note that with the electrolyte present and no current flowing the potential gradient in the bulk of the solution is zero. This has to be the case, for where would the K$^+$ go to if they were being continually dragged towards the cathode?

Triple layer

Fig. 2.14 which shows a family of γ/E curves for different electrolytes demonstrates a failure of the theories described so far. On our present theory all 1:1 electrolytes should behave the same. This is found to be the case when ϕ_Δ is negative but, alas, when ϕ_Δ is positive the salts separate out on to different curves. The reason for this is that the cations remain hydrated; for negative ϕ_Δ they line up correctly on the outer Helmholtz plane and we get a properly behaved Helmholtz layer. For positive ϕ_Δ the anions can become dehydrated and thereby get closer to the electrode. If this is the case they line up (as one might expect) on the *inner Helmholtz plane*. Each anion does this to a different extent and hence the divergence of the curves; F$^-$ is strongly enough hydrated to be well behaved. This specific adsorption of the anions in this way can lead to more complicated potential distributions as sketched in Fig. 2.20 giving a triple layer.

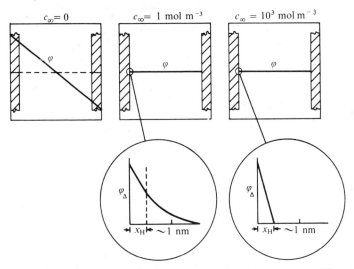

FIG. 2.19. Distribution of potential between two electrodes for three different concentrations of electrolyte.

Effect on electrode kinetics

We have now obtained a description of the variation of potential with distance close to the electrode, which is supported by experiment, and can proceed to see what effect this will have on the study of electrode kinetics. Many workers have contributed to our understanding of this problem, but particular mention must be made of the great Russian electrochemist A. N. Frumkin whose research papers on this topic started in the 1920s and continue to the present day. The most important feature is the separation of the potential drop into that across the Helmholtz layer and that across the diffuse layer. Molecules that are in the diffuse layer are too far away from the electrode to react; they have to get at least as close as the outer Helmholtz plane. At the outer Helmholtz plane the concentrations may well be different from those beyond the double layer as shown in Fig. 2.8. Also the potential available to drive the reaction will not be $(\phi_M - \phi_S)$ but will be roughly $(\phi_M - \phi_H)$. So it appears that we must allow for both these effects. However we can simplify the situation by writing the electrode reaction:

$$O_* \quad \rightleftarrows \quad O_\ddagger \quad \overset{\overset{k_1}{\underset{k_{-1}}{\rightleftarrows}}}{\overset{e^-}{}} \quad R_\ddagger \quad \rightleftarrows \quad R_*$$

		Diffusion	Electron transfer	Diffusion	
Charge on ion		z_O	z_O	z_R	z_R
Location		Just outside the double layer	At the electrode		Just outside the double layer
Potential		ϕ_S	$\phi_\ddagger$	$\phi_\ddagger$	ϕ_S.

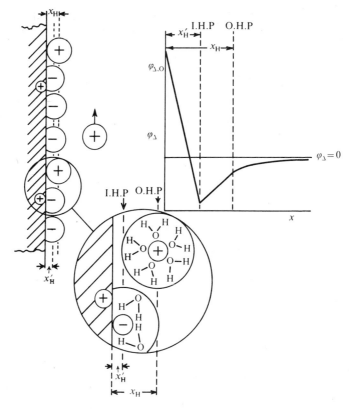

FIG. 2.20. Schematic diagram of triple layer with a layer of specifically adsorbed anions. As shown in the inset they are de-solvated. In the case shown the strong adsorption of the anions leads to a reversal of potential in the double layer. The cations (see inset) remain fully solvated and cannot approach closer than the outer Helmholtz plane. I.H.P. stands for inner Helmholtz plane. The problem of what O.H.P. stands for is left to the reader.

The reaction is a general redox reaction of the form:

$$O + e^- \rightleftarrows R$$

e.g.

$$Fe^{3+} + e^- \rightleftarrows Fe^{2+}.$$

The subscript * indicates species just outside the double layer; the subscript ‡ indicates species which are at the electrode at the right distance for the electrode reaction. Now the diffuse double layer is small enough (~ 1 nm) for there to be equilibrium between O_* and $O_{\ddagger}$ and between R_* and $R_{\ddagger}$. That is, species diffuse to and fro across the diffuse double layer much more often than they react at the electrode. Thus for the reaction of O we have:

$$O_* \quad \rightleftharpoons \quad O_{\ddagger} \quad \longrightarrow$$

Pre-equilibrium   Rate-determining step

Because of this equilibrium from (2.8)

$$[O]_{\ddagger} = [O]_* \exp\left[\frac{-z_0 F(\phi_{\ddagger} - \phi_S)}{RT}\right].$$

As discussed in Chapter 1

$$k_1' = (k_1')_{\phi_M = \phi_{\ddagger}} \exp\left[\frac{-\alpha_1 F(\phi_M - \phi_{\ddagger})}{RT}\right]$$

where we have replaced ϕ_S with $\phi_{\ddagger}$ and the subscript 1 in α_1 distinguishes it from the observed α defined in (1.20). Then we obtain that for the rate of O to R

$$O \overset{\text{rate}}{\rightarrow} R = k_1'[O]_{\ddagger} = (k_1')_{\phi_M = \phi_{\ddagger}} \exp\left[\frac{-\alpha_1 F \Delta\phi}{RT}\right] f_{DL}[O]_* \qquad (2.25)$$

where

$$f_{DL} = \exp\left[\frac{(\alpha_1 - z_0)F(\phi_{\ddagger} - \phi_S)}{RT}\right]. \qquad (2.26)$$

The purpose of separating the exponentials in this way is that f_{DL} is then a double-layer correction. When $\phi_{\ddagger} = \phi_S, f_{DL} = 1$ and (2.25) is the same as the first term in (1.16); changes in $\Delta\phi$ can be measured by varying the potential difference of the whole cell.

For the reverse reaction we obtain by exactly the same argument

$$R \overset{\text{rate}}{\rightarrow} O = k_{-1}'[R]_{\ddagger} = (k_{-1}')_{\phi_M = \phi_{\ddagger}} \exp\frac{\beta_1 F \Delta\phi}{RT} f_{DL}[R]_*$$

where

$$f_{DL} = \exp\left[\frac{(-\beta_1 - z_R)F(\phi_{\ddagger} - \phi_S)}{RT}\right]$$

and, since $z_0 = z_R + 1$ and $\beta_1 = 1 - \alpha_1$, $-\beta_1 - z_R = \alpha_1 - z_0$.

Thus there is the same double layer correction in each rate expression. This must be the case or else we would not obtain the Nernst equation as we did in Chapter 1. The expression f_{DL} can be thought of as the effect on the transition state of the difference in potential between the bulk of the solution, ϕ_S and the plane close to the electrode where the transition state has to be in order to react, $\phi_{\ddagger}$; both the forward and backward reactions pass through the same transition state and hence the correction is the same.

It is tempting to put $\phi_\ddagger = \phi_H$ and assume that the ions react at the outer Helmholtz plane. Although this may not be strictly true we shall succumb to the temptation. Hence we shall consider

$$f_{DL} = \exp\left[\frac{(\alpha_1 - z_0)F(\phi_H - \phi_S)}{RT}\right] = \exp[2(\alpha_1 - z_0)\theta_H]. \qquad (2.27)$$

Effect of f_{DL} on the order of a reaction

In eqn (1.18) we defined the order of an electrochemical reaction. For the simple picture presented there the orders of the Fe^{2+} or Fe^{3+} reactions would each have been unity with respect to Fe^{2+} or Fe^{3+}. Unfortunately however for a binary electrolyte even though we keep $\Delta\phi$ constant, the changes in concentration of the reactant also cause changes in the distribution of the potential difference in $\Delta\phi$ in the double layer. Thus $(\phi_H - \phi_S)$ is also a function of the concentration; f_{DL} becomes more important as the concentration decreases, the contribution from the diffuse layer cannot be neglected, and the change in potential across it becomes larger.

In Appendix 3 we derive the relationship

$$m_0 = 1 + \frac{(z_0 - \alpha_1)C'_{DL,0}\sinh\theta_H}{C'_H + C'_{DL,0}\cosh\theta_H}. \qquad (2.28)$$

Now when θ_H is small and $C'_{DL,0}$ is smaller than C'_H the second correcting term is negligible. But unfortunately, when studies are made away from the potential of zero charge, θ_H is large, the hyperbolic terms dominate the expression, and the apparent order is

$$m_0 = 1 \pm (z_0 - \alpha_1). \qquad (2.29)$$

Table 2.2 gives results for $\alpha_1 = \frac{1}{2}$ and different values of z_0.

TABLE 2.2

Apparent order from (2.28) for reduction of O for
$$\alpha_1 = \frac{1}{2}$$

z_0	$\theta_H \gg 1$	$\theta_H = 0$	$\theta_H \ll -1$
2	$2\frac{1}{2}$	1	$-\frac{1}{2}$
1	$1\frac{1}{2}$	1	$\frac{1}{2}$
−1	$-\frac{1}{2}$	1	$2\frac{1}{2}$
−2	$-1\frac{1}{2}$	1	$3\frac{1}{2}$

Near the potential of zero charge all is well, but this will be a relatively narrow range of potential, corresponding to that of the sharp minima in Fig. 2.16. At other potentials (2.29) will hold. The values in Table 2.2 have been confirmed experimentally. For example the reduction of H^+ in dilute solutions of acid appears to be half-order in $[H^+]$.

Effect of f_{DL} on slope of Tafel plot

We now consider the effect of f_{DL} on α the slope of the Tafel plot which describes the effect of the applied potential on the rate of reaction.

From Appendix (3)

$$\alpha \simeq \alpha_1 + \frac{(z_0 - \alpha_1)}{1 + (C'_{DL,0}/C'_H)\cosh\theta_H}. \tag{2.30}$$

In this case when $|\theta_H|$ is large the cosh term makes the correcting term negligible. In the vicinity of E_{zc} where θ_H is small

$$\alpha \simeq \alpha_1 + \frac{z_0 - \alpha_1}{1 + C'_{DL,0}/C'_H} = \frac{C'_{DL,0}\alpha_1 + C'_H z_0}{C'_{DL,0} + C'_H} \tag{2.31}$$

and α will lie between α_1 and z_0 depending on the relative sizes of $C'_{DL,0}$ and C'_H. If z_0 is negative, that is one is reducing an anion, then α can even be negative. For instance if $C'_H = C'_{DL,0}$, $\alpha_1 = \frac{1}{2}$ and $z_0 = -1$, $\alpha = -\frac{1}{2}$. This seems most surprising. It means that even if the electrode is made more negative the current from reducing O decreases. Fig. 2.21 shows some calculations by Parsons which exhibit these features; the capacitances are those for NaF at a Hg electrode. This effect arises because the charge is spread out in the diffuse layer rather than being concentrated in the Helmholtz layer. The negative charge in the diffuse layer repels the negative ions from the electrode and is not available to drive the electrode reaction. Indeed for concentrations below 20 mole m^{-3} the electrode can pass the same current at three different potentials. This is shown in the three insets of Fig. 2.21. The middle inset is the simple case at the potential of zero charge. (Although the electrode is uncharged electrochemical reactions can still take place and do not forget that there may still be a potential drop at the actual interface due to the solvent dipoles etc.) When $i = i_{ZC}$ at more positive potentials the electrochemical rate constant for the reduction is several thousand times slower but the concentration compensates for this by being several thousand times larger as the negative ions are attracted towards the electrode. The opposite happens at negative potentials; the rate constant is several thousand times larger but the reactant ions are strongly repelled from the electrode. When the ion to be reduced is positively charged (broken line in Fig. 2.21) the effects are much less dramatic even when $c_\infty = 1$ mol m^{-3}.

The minima, seen in Fig. 2.21, have been found in the reduction of such ions as $S_2O_8^{2-}$ and $Fe(CN)_6^{3-}$ and also in the oxidation of Eu^{2+}. In Frumkin's work on $S_2O_8^{2-}$, the reaction has been studied on Pt, Cu, Hg, Pb, and Cd electrodes; the reduction in current with increasing negative potential correlates well with the different potentials of zero charge for the different metals. Fig. 2.22 shows some of Frumkin's results.

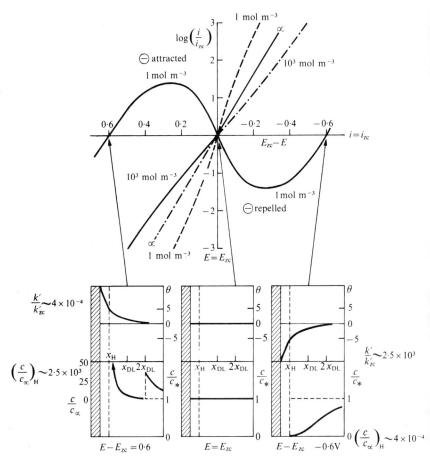

FIG. 2.21. Variation of $\log c'$ with potential for the reduction of a singly charged anion at two different concentrations (——) and of a singly charged cation at $1 \, mol \, m^{-3}$ (– – – – –). Insets show potential and concentration distribution for the anion at $1 \, mol \, m^{-3}$ for $i = i_{zc}$ where i_{zc} is the current at the potential of zero charge. Data from R. Parsons, *Adv. Electrochem. Engng.*, 1961, **1**, 34.

Addition of supporting electrolyte

The results discussed in the last two sections show the difficulties of studying electrode kinetics in solutions of binary electrolytes. Even the most ingenious kineticist would find it hard to devise mechanisms with negative orders and negative values of α. The explanation of the results in terms of the

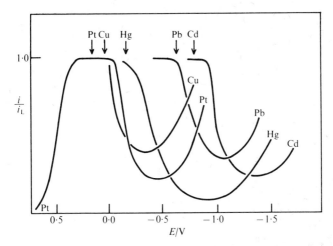

FIG. 2.22. Frumkin's results for reduction of $S_2O_8^{2-}$ at rotating disc electrodes of various metals. In all cases solution was 1 mol m^{-3} in $K_2S_2O_8$ and 1 mol m^{-3} in Na$_2$SO$_4$. Arrows indicate potentials of zero charge for different metals.

potential distribution in the double layer is satisfactory and the agreement between theory and experiment confirms the model and our understanding of the electrode–solution interface. But the kineticist wishes to investigate the mechanisms of reactions rather than the structure of the double layer, and so to minimize the effect of the diffuse layer he adds a large concentration of inert electrolyte. Typically he studies reactions in concentrations of inert electrolyte of about 1 mol dm^{-3}, while the concentrations of the reactive species at the electrode are about 1 mol m^{-3}. Hence in investigating the order of the electrochemical reaction, the changes of the order of 1 mol m^{-3} in the reactant concentration do not change the potential distribution in the double layer; it is fixed by the much larger concentration ($\sim$ 1 mol dm^{-3}) of the inert electrolyte (NaClO$_4$, KCl etc.). So in the presence of the supporting electrolyte f_{DL} does not change, and the true order can be measured. In the analysis of the Tafel slope the large concentration of electrolyte increases $C_{DL,0}$ and hence diminishes the correcting function in (2.38). Fig. 2.8 shows that for $c_\infty = 1$ mol dm^{-3},

$$C'_{DL,0} \gg C'_H$$

and so

$$\alpha \simeq \alpha_1. \tag{2.31}$$

Hence the main message from this chapter is that the study of electrode kinetics must be carried out in the presence of an excess of inert electrolyte. This electrolyte serves two purposes. Firstly it carries the current in the bulk of the solution and there is only a small potential difference due to 'iR' drop. The observed potential difference is concentrated at the electrode solution interfaces. Secondly, it increases the capacity of the diffuse layer so that at the electrode the potential drop is confined to the Helmholtz layer and does not spread out into the diffuse layer (case I of Table 2.1 and case 3 of Fig. 2.18). Thus all the potential difference at the electrode solution interface is available for affecting the actual rate of the electrode reaction. There are no complicating features from the interaction of the ions with the charge on the electrode at a distance where they cannot react.

One could perhaps have merely stated this recipe, but the more detailed understanding of the double layer and the variation of potential is valuable in describing reactions at the electrode. Furthermore the success of the model confirms the principles underlying the Debye–Hückel theory of electrolytes. It is also in its own right a satisfying theory which explains successfully some rather peculiar results such as the minima in the capacitance curves in Fig. 2.17 and the negative values of α in Fig. 2.22.

3. Techniques for measuring electrode reactions

Introduction

THE title to this chapter could well serve for a never-ending series of volumes which would keep the editor in claret for the rest of his days. Instead of a breathless tour of all the different electrochemical techniques we will concentrate in this chapter on four of the most important. We start by considering the effects of the depletion of the electrode reactant close to the electrode and how the reactant reaches the electrode from the bulk of the solution. In particular we see how these problems can be calculated for the rotating disc electrode; this electrode is particularly simple in that a steady state is established. There follows a discussion on the relative roles of kinetics and transport in determining the rates not only of electrode reactions but also ordinary homogeneous processes such as proton transfers. The next problem is the description of the complete current voltage curve and its separation into two types, reversible and irreversible, corresponding to the cases where the behaviour is controlled respectively by the thermodynamics or by the kinetics of the system. There is then a brief digression into the effects of impurities on the classical determination of e.m.f.s and how these effects are linked to the kinetics of the electrode process. The dropping mercury electrode is described and compared with the rotating disc electrode; we then discuss how to plot a corrected Tafel plot from the experimental data to obtain the kinetic parameters. These methods are suitable for slow reactions but the chapter ends with two relaxation techniques which can be used to study fast electrode reactions.

Transport to the electrode

In Chapter 1 we were careful to add the subscript 0 to the concentrations to express the fact that the rate of the reaction at the electrode will depend on the concentration of the species at the electrode surface and this concentration may not be the same as the concentration of the species in the bulk of the solution, denoted by the subscript ∞. In the last chapter the 0 was changed to $a*$ in (2.25) where $[X]_*$ is the concentration of X just outside the double layer at a distance of ~ 1 to 10 nm from the electrode. Is $[X]_* = [X]_\infty$? If it were then we could substitute $[X]_* = [X]_\infty$ in (2.25). This equation would then predict that on increasing the potential the current–voltage curve would have the form shown in Fig. 3.1. Following Rossetti we ask 'does the curve wind uphill all the way?' She replies 'yes to the very end', but in our case the answer is no. The typical form of a current voltage curve that is actually observed is also shown in Fig. 3.1. However to observe such a nice curve one has to use the proper type of electrode. If one just sticks a stationary electrode

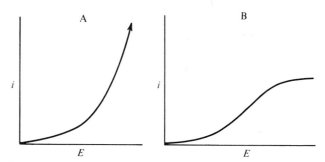

FIG. 3.1. Current–voltage curve according to eqn (2.25) with $[X]_*$ constant showing exponential increase; and a real current–voltage curve.

into an unstirred beaker then one would observe the results shown in Fig. 3.2. This type of experiment used to be performed at Oxford by unfortunate undergraduates. The only useful result that was obtained was the Albery equation

$$i = f\left(N_W, L, \frac{\partial (JD)}{\partial t}\right) \tag{3.1}$$

where

N_W is the number of windows open in the laboratory,

L the number of lorries passing,

and

$\dfrac{\partial (JD)}{\partial t}$ a periodic function describing the supervision of a typical junior demonstrator.

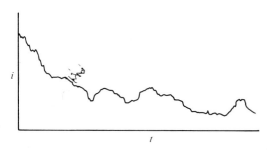

FIG. 3.2. Typical results for current against time from passing current between stationary electrodes in an unstirred beaker.

The reason for the results in Fig. 3.2 and for eqn (3.1) is that $[X]_*$ is not constant. As X reacts on the electrode its concentration near the electrode is depleted and becomes less than that in the bulk of the solution. Hence for a successful study of electrode kinetics we have to be able to describe $[X]_*$ in terms of $[X]_\infty$.

To do this we must choose experimental conditions where the transport of X from the bulk of the solution to the electrode is well-defined and if possible we would like to be able to calculate that transport theoretically. The rotating disc electrode fulfils both these conditions. Other types of electrode system (for example rotating wires) have well-defined transport but are difficult to describe theoretically.

Hydrodynamics of rotating disc electrode

A rotating disc electrode (R.D.E.) is drawn in Fig. 3.3. The system is described in cylindrical polar coordinates ϕ, r, and x, as shown. For this system von Karman calculated the exact pattern of flow set up in the solution by the spinning disc. The velocities of flow along the three coordinates are given by:

$$v_\phi = r\omega\Phi(x/x_{Hy})$$
$$v_r = r\omega\mathscr{R}(x/x_{Hy})$$
$$v_x = (\omega v)^{\frac{1}{2}}X(x/x_{Hy}) \tag{3.2}$$

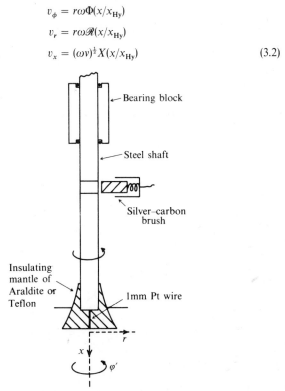

FIG. 3.3. A rotating disc electrode of the Riddiford design. The electrode is the polished end of a Pt wire of 1 to 3 mm radius. The coordinate system is also shown.

where

v is in m s^{-1}

ω is the rotation speed in radians s^{-1}

v ($= \eta/\rho$) is the kinematic viscosity in m^2 s^{-1}

Φ, $\mathscr{R}$, and X are functions of x/x_{Hy}

x_{Hy} is thickness of the hydrodynamic layer in m,

and

$$x_{Hy} = (v/\omega)^{\frac{1}{2}}. \tag{3.3}$$

Typical values of x_{Hy} are 0·1 to 1 mm. The functions Φ, $\mathscr{R}$, and $-X$ are plotted in Fig. 3.4. The negative sign in v_x arises because the solution is flowing towards the disc. The qualitative pattern of flow is that on the disc surface $\Phi = 1$ with $\mathscr{R}$ and $X = 0$. That is, the solution next to the disc spins round with it. The spinning motion (Φ) is gradually quenched as one moves further away from the disc. However the spinning motion does induce radial flow so that $\mathscr{R}$ increases to a maximum when $x \sim x_{Hy}$. Here the spinning solution is being flung out centrifugally. This solution is replaced from below by a stream flowing towards the electrode. Hence as the spinning motion and centrifugal motion are quenched far from the electrode they are replaced by a constant flow of $-X$ towards the electrode. The whole disc acts as a pump sucking solution towards it, spinning it around, and flinging it out sideways. The particularly good feature of the rotating disc system is that from eqn (3.2) the x component of the velocity, which brings fresh solution to the electrode, depends only on x and does not depend on r. Hence in any plane parallel to the disc

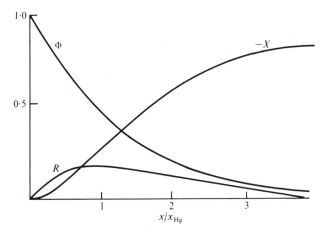

FIG. 3.4. The hydrodynamics of an R.D.E. Plots against distance from the electrode of Φ, R, and $-X$ describing respectively the angular flow, the centrifugal flow, and the flow towards the electrode.

surface v_x is constant as shown in Fig. 3.5. It is this unique feature of the rotating disc system that makes its mathematical treatment much easier than other electrode systems.

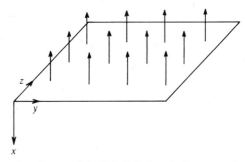

FIG. 3.5. The unique feature of the R.D.E. is that the flow towards the electrode is the same in any plane that is parallel to the electrode.

Transport to an R.D.E.

The problem of transport to an R.D.E. was first solved by the distinguished Russian scientist Levich. The basic differential equation is

$$\frac{\partial c}{\partial t} \; = \; D\frac{\partial^2 c}{\partial x^2} \; - \; v_x\frac{\partial c}{\partial x}.$$

Variation of   Transport by   Transport by
c with time   diffusion   convection

The first two terms are Fick's second law of diffusion which is explained in Fig. 3.6; the third term describes the transport of material to the disc by the

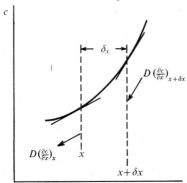

FIG. 3.6. Fick's second law of diffusion. Across unit area

$$\delta c = \delta t \times \left[D\left(\frac{\partial c}{\partial x}\right)_{x+\delta x} - D\left(\frac{\partial c}{\partial x}\right)_x \right] \quad \text{or} \quad \frac{\partial c}{\partial t} = D\frac{\partial^2 c}{\partial x^2}.$$

forced flow imposed by the spinning of the disc. It is depicted in Fig. 3.7. Owing to the uniform nature of v_x (Fig. 3.5) we do not have to include terms in $\partial/\partial r$ since c will vary only with x.

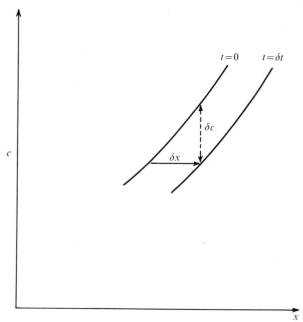

FIG. 3.7. Transport by convection. Across unit area

$$\delta c = -\delta x(\partial c/\partial x). \text{ But } \delta x = v_x \, \delta t \text{ and so } \frac{\partial c}{\partial t} = -v_x \frac{\partial c}{\partial x}.$$

Now we are interested in the steady-state solution. That is when $\partial c/\partial t = 0$ and material is being transported at a steady rate to the electrode where it is reacting. Hence

$$D\frac{\partial^2 c}{\partial x^2} = v_x \frac{\partial c}{\partial x}. \tag{3.4}$$

This equation has to have the boundary condition that far away from the electrode as $x \to \infty$ $c \to c_\infty$. Integration of the equation with this boundary condition is carried out in Appendix (4) and gives the result

$$\left(\frac{\partial c}{\partial x}\right)_{x=0} = \frac{c_\infty - c_0}{x_D} \tag{3.5}$$

where

$$x_D = 0.643W^{-\frac{1}{2}}v^{\frac{1}{6}}D^{\frac{1}{3}} \tag{3.6}$$

and W is the rotation speed measured in Hz.

Eqn (3.5) is the vital connection between the concentration gradient at the surface of the electrode, the surface concentration and the bulk concentration. The value of x_D can be calculated from eqn (3.6) knowing W, v, and D.

Fig. 3.8 shows a typical plot of the full *Levich equation* derived in Appendix (4) for c as a function of x. It can be seen how the distance x_D divides the concentration profile into two regions. For $x < x_D$ transport is by diffusion across the stagnant layer of solution that is swept round by the electrode. For $x > x_D$ there is sufficient motion of the fluid for the solution to be well stirred and the concentration is uniform. The distance x_D is therefore called the *thickness of the diffusion layer*.

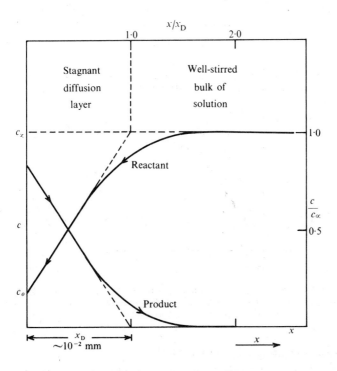

FIG. 3.8. Variation of concentration with distance from a R.D.E. for the reactant and the product. Note that x_D is the thickness of the diffusion layer and that the concentration gradient at the electrode surface (at $x = 0$) is $(c_\infty - c_0)/x_D$.

Fig. 3.9 shows values of x_D as a function of the rotation speed for $D = 1\ m^2\ Gs^{-1}\ (10^{-5}\ cm^2\ s^{-1})$ and $v = 1\ m^2\ Ms^{-1}\ (10^{-2}\ cm^2\ s^{-1})$. The faster the electrode is rotated the more thoroughly stirred is the solution and the narrower is the stagnant layer. This results in a steeper concentration gradient across the stagnant layer and faster transport to the electrode. Fig. 3.10 shows the effect of increasing the rotation speed by a factor of 4; this halves x_D.

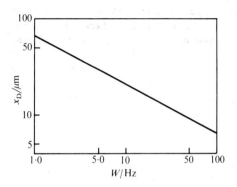

FIG. 3.9. Variation of x_D, the diffusion layer thickness, with W the rotation speed for typical values of D and v appropriate to H_2O at 298 K.

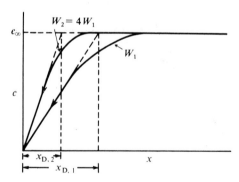

FIG. 3.10. Effect on x_D and concentration profile of changing the rotation speed from W_1 to $W_2 = 4W_1$; x_D is halved and the transport limited flux j_L is doubled. The transport limited flux is when $c_* = 0$ as shown.

Summary of different layers on R.D.E.

At this stage it is helpful to summarize the different layers that are present on an R.D.E. and their thicknesses. This is done in Fig. 3.11. The difference in several orders of magnitude between the widths of the double layer and the

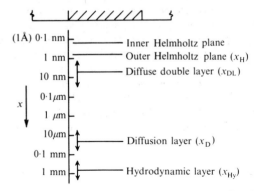

(1Å) 0·1 nm ──── Inner Helmholtz plane
1 nm ──── Outer Helmholtz plane (x_H)
10 nm ──── Diffuse double layer (x_{DL})
0·1 μm
x 1 μm
10 μm ──── Diffusion layer (x_D)
0·1 mm
1 mm ──── Hydrodynamic layer (x_{Hy})

FIG. 3.11. Summary of different layers below a rotating disc electrode.

diffusion layer means that we can measure x in the transport problem from just outside the double layer and so (3.5) becomes:

$$\left(\frac{\partial c}{\partial x}\right)_* = \frac{c_\infty - c_*}{x_D}. \tag{3.7}$$

Current–voltage curve

We now enquire what happens when a species is reduced on the electrode with a rate constant k' given by

$$k' = k'_{E=0} \exp\left(-\frac{\alpha FE}{RT}\right). \tag{3.8}$$

In the steady state the flux of material reacting at the electrode surface must equal the flux being transported through the diffusion layer and arriving on the outside of the double layer. Hence

$$j = k'c_* \quad \text{for the electrode reaction} \tag{3.9}$$

and

$$j = D\left(\frac{\partial c}{\partial x}\right)_* = \frac{D}{x_D}(c_\infty - c_*) \quad \text{for the transport.} \tag{3.10}$$

Elimination of j gives

$$c_* = \frac{c_\infty}{1 + (k'x_D/D)} \tag{3.11}$$

and of c_* gives

$$\frac{1}{j} = \frac{1}{k'c_\infty} + \frac{1}{Dc_\infty/x_D}. \tag{3.12}$$

Hence the flux is mainly determined by the *smaller* of the two terms in this equation. The two different extremes are summarized in Table 3.1. A plot of $\log j$ versus the applied e.m.f. is shown in Fig. 3.12. The curve does not wind uphill all the way but reaches a steady value when the electrode is made very reducing. The electrode is then so active that every O which reaches it is immediately reduced; this is why under these conditions $c_* \ll c_\infty$. The concentration profile is similar to those in Fig. 3.10, and the current is solely determined by the supply of O to the electrode. The steady value of the current corresponding to this flux is called the *limiting current*; we shall denote this by the subscript L. Hence

$$j_L = \frac{Dc_\infty}{x_D} \tag{3.13}$$

and

$$i_L = nFAj_L. \tag{3.14}$$

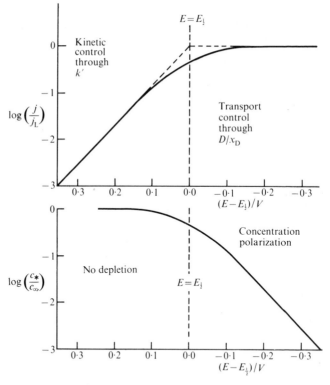

FIG. 3.12. Current–voltage curve according to eqn. (3.12). Also shown is the variation in c_*, the concentration just outside the double layer, according to eqn (3.11). $E_{\frac{1}{2}}$ is the half-wave potential where $j = \frac{1}{2}j_L$.

TABLE 3.1
Kinetic versus transport control

Kinetic control	Transport control
$D/x_D \gg k'$	$k' \gg D/x_D$
$j = k'c_\infty$	$j = Dc_\infty/x_D$
$\dfrac{\partial \ln j}{\partial(-E)} = \dfrac{\alpha F}{RT}$	$\dfrac{\partial \ln j}{\partial(-E)} = 0$
$\dfrac{\partial j}{\partial W^{\frac{1}{2}}} = 0$	$\dfrac{\partial j}{\partial W^{\frac{1}{2}}} = \text{constant}$
$c_* = c_\infty$	$c_* \ll c_\infty$

Limiting currents and rotation speed

Since from (3.14) and (3.6) $i_L \propto x_D^{-1}$ and $x_D \propto W^{-\frac{1}{2}}$ we should find that

$$i_L = BW^{\frac{1}{2}}, \tag{3.15}$$

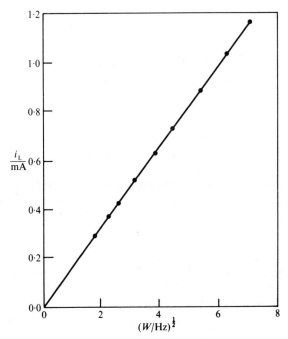

FIG. 3.13. Typical results for limiting current on a R.D.E. from $I^- \rightarrow \frac{1}{2}I_2 + e^-$, as a function of rotation speed plotted according to eqn (3.15).

where

$$B = 1{\cdot}554nFAD^{\frac{2}{3}}v^{-\frac{1}{6}}c_{\infty}.$$

Many workers have found that (3.15) holds for many different systems. Fig. 3.13 shows some typical results. When both D and c_{∞} are known the observed and calculated values of B are found to agree to within 1 or 2 per cent, thus proving the theory of the R.D.E. If either D or c_{∞} are unknown then either may be determined from measurements of B. Thus the R.D.E. can be used to determine diffusion coefficients and it can be used as an analytical technique for determining concentrations. The determination of concentrations in this manner is called polarography and it depends upon the principle that the limiting current for any species is proportional to its concentration (see below).

Analysis in terms of k'_D

The mathematical description presented so far has calculated the full concentration profile with respect to distance. The results can however be presented according to a more familiar kinetic scheme. If in homogeneous kinetics we have a reaction scheme of the form

$$A \underset{k_{-1}}{\overset{k_1}{\rightleftarrows}} B \overset{k_2}{\rightarrow} ,$$

then if we apply the steady state approximation to B we obtain that

$$\text{rate} = j_{\ddagger} = \frac{k_1 k_2 [A]}{k_{-1} + k_2},$$

or

$$\frac{1}{j_{\ddagger}} = \frac{k_{-1}}{k_1 k_2 [A]} + \frac{1}{k_1 [A]},$$

where $j_{\ddagger}$ is the flux through the transition state (mol m^{-3} s^{-1}). Depending on the relative size of k_{-1} and k_2 we have two possible approximations:

$k_{-1} \gg k_2$	$k_2 \gg k_{-1}$
$j_{\ddagger} = \dfrac{k_1}{k_{-1}} k_2 [A]$	$j_{\ddagger} = k_1 [A]$
Pre-equilibrium Second step rate-determining	First step rate-determining Second step fast

Now let us write the electrochemical scheme

$$O_{\infty} \underset{k'_D}{\overset{k'_D}{\rightleftarrows}} O_* \overset{k'_1}{\rightarrow}$$

Bulk of   Diffusion   Just outside   Electrode
solution   double layer   reaction

Then by just the same argument

$$\frac{1}{j} = \frac{k'_D}{k'_1 k'_D [O]_\infty} + \frac{1}{k'_D [O]_\infty}$$

$$= \frac{1}{k'_1 [O]_\infty} + \frac{1}{k'_D [O]_\infty}. \tag{3.16}$$

Comparing this with (3.12) we find that if

$$k'_D = D/x_D \tag{3.17}$$

then (3.12) and (3.16) are identical.

Like the heterogeneous rate constant k'_1, k'_D has the dimensions of $m\,s^{-1}$ since it describes a flux in $mol\,m^2\,s^{-1}$ in terms of a concentration in $mol\,m^{-3}$. Eqn (3.17) is entirely sensible in the way that the rate constant for crossing the stagnant layer depends on D, the diffusion coefficient, and x_D the thickness of the layer.

Indeed the flux through the layer can be regarded as the difference between O_∞ trying to reach the electrode and O_* trying to get away:

$$j = k'_D [O]_\infty - k'_D [O]_*. \tag{3,18}$$

Since

$$j = D \left(\frac{\partial [O]}{\partial x} \right)_*$$

this equation agrees with (3.10). Furthermore at the limiting current $[O]_* = 0$ because it reacts so fast at the electrode. Hence

$$j_L = k'_D [O]_\infty. \tag{3.19}$$

Substituting in (3.16) we obtain another form of the equation

$$\frac{j}{j_L} = \frac{1}{1 + (k'_D/k'_1)}. \tag{3.20}$$

The previous discussion applies as to the relative sizes of k'_1 and k'_D:

$k'_D \gg k'_1$	$k'_1 \gg k'_D$
Diffusion layer in equilibrium rate-determining step at electrode	Transport rate-determining electrode step very fast.
$j = k'_1 [O]_\infty$	$j = k'_D [O]_\infty$
	$= j_L$

Note that not only can the electrochemist alter k'_1 by varying the potential but the electrochemist with an R.D.E. can alter k'_D by varying the rotation speed. The message should be obvious.

This analysis in terms of k'_D can be applied to any electrode where a reproducible stagnant layer is established. Other types of electrodes, that have been
used, are, for instance, a rotating wire or a tube electrode with the solution
flowing through a tube, of which a cylindrical section of the wall serves as
the electrode. The calculation of k'_D however is more complicated for these
other systems. The advantage of the R.D.E. as shown in Fig. 3.5 is that there
is uniform transport to the surface.

Thermal and diffusion control

The pattern of behaviour depicted in Fig. 3.12 is also found in homogeneous
kinetics. For instance proton transfer reactions can be controlled either by
the actual proton transfer or by the diffusion together of the reactants. We can
write

$$S + HA \underset{k_{-D}}{\overset{k_D}{\rightleftharpoons}} S\,HA \overset{k_1}{\rightarrow} \text{ products}$$

and as discussed above

$$\frac{1}{k_{obs}} = \frac{1}{k_D} + \frac{k_{-D}}{k_D k_1}$$

When $k_{-D} \gg k_1$ the proton transfer is rate determining, but when $k_1 \gg k_{-D}$
the reaction is diffusion controlled. A plot of log k against pK gives a Brønsted
plot in the region where the proton transfer is rate determining and a plateau
when the reaction is diffusion controlled. This is shown for some of Eigen's
results in Fig. 3.14. The current–voltage curve of Fig. 3.12 exhibits exactly
the same type of pattern for the same reasons. Thus both in homogeneous
kinetics and in electrode kinetics alteration of the reactivity of the reactant HA
or of the electrode can cause the rate determining step to shift from the proton

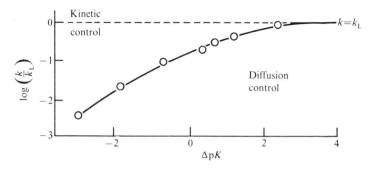

FIG. 3.14. Shift in rate determining step for typical proton transfer reaction,
$C_6H_5OH + B \rightarrow C_6H_5O^- + HB^+$: $\Delta pK = pK_{HB} - pK_{C_6H_5OH}$ and k_L is the transport
limited rate constant of 3×10^9 dm^3 mol^{-1} s^{-1}.

or electron transfer to the transport of S and HA together or the transport of O to the electrode. The homogeneous kineticist has to have a shelf full of little brown bottles each containing a different acid or base. The electrochemist merely alters his potentiometer. Do not forget that a change of 1 V shifts the kinetics of a single-electron transfer by $\sim 10^8$ and the thermodynamics by $\sim 10^{17}$; this is more than the difference between H_3O^+ and OH^- as acids.

Current–voltage curve for O, R system

So far for the rotating disc electrode we have only considered a system where the reduction of O is taking place. We now consider the full system

$$O + e^- \underset{k'_{-1}}{\overset{k'_1}{\rightleftarrows}} R.$$

To simplify the algebra we assume that the diffusion coefficients of O and R are equal; diffusion coefficients are mainly determined by molecular volume and so this is a good approximation. Then we may write in the steady state

$$j = k'_1[O]_* - k'_{-1}[R]_* \qquad O \rightleftarrows R \text{ at electrode}$$

$$= k'_D([O]_\infty - [O]_*) \qquad \text{Diffusion of O towards electrode}$$

$$= k'_D([R]_* - [R]_\infty). \qquad \text{Diffusion of R away from electrode.}$$

We will also write the limiting fluxes for O and R as

$$j_O = k'_D[O]_\infty \quad \text{and} \quad j_R = k'_D[R]_\infty.$$

Eliminating the four concentrations from these five equations we obtain:

$$j = \frac{j_O k'_1 - j_R k'_{-1}}{k'_D + k'_1 + k'_{-1}} \tag{3.21}$$

We can achieve a further simplification of this equation. Since k'_1 increases as E becomes more negative and k'_{-1} decreases, there must be some potential where the two are equal. What is it? Well if we had equal concentrations of O and R (neglecting as always activity effects) then $j_O = j_R$ and if $k'_1 = k'_{-1}$ then $j = 0$. But thermodynamics tells us (see (1.17)) that for equal concentrations of O and R

$$j = 0 \quad \text{when} \quad E = E^\ominus \quad \text{with respect to the normal hydrogen electrode.}$$

So for the O, R redox system we can write

$$k'_1 = k'_0 \exp\left(-\frac{\alpha E' F}{RT}\right) \tag{3.22}$$

$$k'_{-1} = k'_0 \exp\left\{\frac{\beta E' F}{RT}\right\} \tag{3.23}$$

where $\alpha + \beta = 1$,

$$E' = (E - E^{\ominus})$$

and E and $E^{\ominus}$ are both measured with respect to the same reference electrode. The parameter k_0' describes the free energy barrier (B) in Fig. 1.5 at the particular potential where $G^{\ominus}$ for O and for R are equal, as shown in Fig. 3.15.†

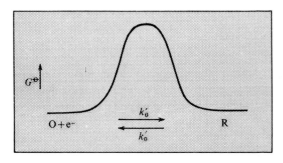

FIG. 3.15. When $E = E^{\ominus}$ the rate constants for the forward and backward reactions are equal. This is section B of Fig. 1.5.

Taking $\alpha = \beta = \frac{1}{2}$ we write as we did in Chapter 2

$$\theta' = \frac{FE'}{2RT} \tag{3.24}$$

and now substituting from (3.22) to (3.24), in (3.21) we obtain:

$$j = \frac{j_0 \exp(-\theta') - j_R \exp(\theta')}{k_D'/k_0' + \exp(-\theta') + \exp(\theta')} \tag{3.25}$$

Fig. 3.16 shows a plot of the equation for the particular case where $j_0 = j_R$ and $k_D'/k_0' = 20$. For all cases, when θ' is large and positive

$$j \rightarrow -j_R,$$

and when θ' is large and negative

$$j \rightarrow j_0.$$

† Black-belt electrochemists like to turn k_0' into a standard exchange-current density i_0, by writing $i_0 = nFk_0'$, but we won't risk being thrown and will stick with the more familiar concept of a rate constant.

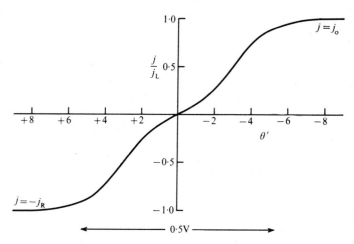

FIG. 3.16. Typical current–voltage curve from eqn. (3.25) for equal concentrations of O and R so that $j_O = j_R$ and for $k'_D/k'_O = 20$.

Thus at extremes of potential j varies between the two limiting fluxes due to the transport of R and O. Near $\theta' = 0$

$$j \simeq \frac{(j_O - j_R) - \theta'(j_O + j_R)}{k'_D/k'_0 + 2} \tag{3.26}$$

giving a linear relation between j and θ'. In this region the size of j is critically dependent on the size of the ratio k'_D/k'_0, and systems are therefore divided into two classes:

$$k'_0 \gg k'_D \quad \text{and} \quad k'_D \gg k'_0.$$
Reversible   Irreversible

The reason for the names may become clearer later on.

Between the linear region near $j = 0$ and the limiting regions at extremes of potential for values of $k'_D/k'_0 > 5$, there will exist a limited region where j depends exponentially on $\pm \theta$. It is over this limited range of potential that the simple Tafel relation discussed in Chapter 1 applies. For larger values of $|\theta'|$ the simple relation breaks down because of the changes in concentration. For smaller values of $|\theta'|$ it breaks down because the reverse reaction is significant. We will discuss first of all the difference between reversible and irreversible systems which depends on the effect of the back reaction. Later on in the chapter we will learn how to correct the observed currents for the effect of changes in concentration and hence extend the range of potential over which a Tafel plot can be made.

Irreversible systems

These are systems where

$$k'_0 \ll k'_D. \tag{3.27}$$

At the potential where $\theta' \sim 0$ ($E \sim E^\ominus$) the barrier to reaction is large; the electrode kinetics are slow compared to diffusion.

From eqns (3.26) and (3.27) at $\theta' = 0$, $j \ll j_O$ or j_R. However by moving the potential away from $\theta' = 0$ sufficiently far in either a positive or a negative direction the electrode reactions can be driven. The $\exp(\pm\theta')$ terms in (3.25) become sufficiently large. But as $\exp(\theta')$ increases $\exp(-\theta')$ decreases and vice versa. So we have for reducing O

$$\exp(-\theta') \gg \exp(\theta')$$

and for oxidizing R

$$\exp(\theta') \gg \exp(-\theta').$$

For systems where current flows only when either of these conditions holds (3.25) can be split into two terms corresponding to the two different inequalities:

$$j = \frac{j_O \exp(-\theta')}{k'_D/k'_0 + \exp(-\theta')} - \frac{j_R \exp(\theta')}{k'_D/k'_0 + \exp(\theta')}. \tag{3.28}$$

When O is being reduced the potential is so negative that R is inactive on the electrode and similarly when R is being oxidized O is inactive.

$E - E^\ominus$	$E - E^\ominus$
negative	positive
$\theta' < -3$	$\theta' > 3$
O → R	R → O
but NOT	but NOT
R → O	O → R

Thus the electrode reactions are 'irreversible'. For these systems the back reaction does not interfere in the determination of kinetics from the Tafel plot. Each of the terms in (3.28) has the same form as (3.20), which was indeed derived neglecting R, e.g.

$$j = \frac{j_O}{k'_D/\{k'_0 \exp(-\theta')\} + 1} = \frac{j_L}{(k'_D/k'_1) + 1}.$$

Fig. 3.17 shows a plot of j against potential for the particular case of $j_O = j_R$ and $k'_0/k'_D = 10^{-2}$. Also included are schematic concentration and free energy profiles at the different potentials. Fig. 3.18 shows a family of curves for j/j_O

for different values of k'_0/k'_D. All the curves have the same shape but the smaller this quantity is the harder the reaction has to be driven and the more they are shifted from $E^\ominus$. This shift is described by the 'half-wave potential' which is defined as the point where

$$j = \tfrac{1}{2}j_L.$$

These points are shown in Fig. 3.17.

Then for $e^- + O \rightarrow R$

$$\exp(-\theta'_{\frac{1}{2}}) = \frac{k'_D}{k'_0}.$$

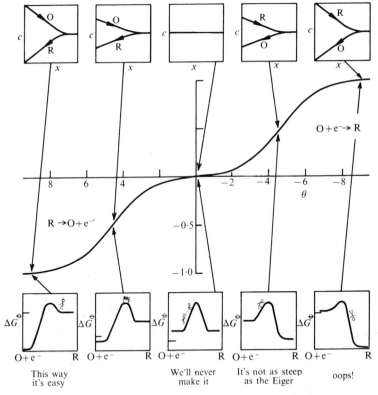

FIG. 3.17. Irreversible current–voltage curve from (3.25) or (3.28) for equal concentrations of O and R so that $j_O = j_R$ and for $k'_0/k'_D = 10^{-2}$. Schematic concentration profiles and free-energy barriers are also shown; $\Delta G^\ominus = G^\ominus - G^\ominus_\ddagger$, so that the transition states are drawn at the same level.

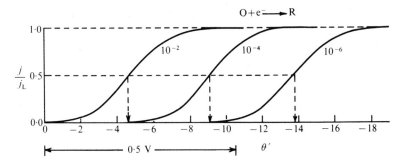

FIG. 3.18. Family of irreversible current–voltage curves for reduction of O from (3.28). Each curve is labelled with value of k'_O/k'_D and the value of θ' corresponding to the half-wave potential is shown. The displacement along the x axis in terms of V is also indicated. Note that the smaller is k'_O the harder the reaction has to be driven.

For $R \longrightarrow O + e^-$

$$\exp(\theta'_{\frac{1}{2}}) = \frac{k'_D}{k'_0}$$

and hence the half-wave potentials are given by

$$E_{\frac{1}{2}} = E^{\ominus} \pm \frac{RT}{F} \ln \frac{k'_D}{k'_0}. \tag{3.29}$$

Note that

$$E_{\frac{1}{2}} \neq E^{\ominus}$$

and that it is a *kinetic* parameter and not a thermodynamic one.

Reversible systems

For these systems $k'_0 \gg k'_D$. Thus in (3.25)

$$\frac{k'_D}{k'_0} \ll 1 < \exp(-\theta') + \exp(\theta')$$

and hence

$$j \simeq \frac{j_O \exp(-\theta') - j_R \exp(\theta')}{\exp(-\theta') + \exp(\theta')}. \tag{3.30}$$

This expression contains no k'_0. The reason for this is that the electrode reaction is now so fast that equilibrium between O_* and R_* is maintained at the electrode:

$$O_* + e^- \rightleftarrows R_*.$$

Hence we have the term '*reversible*'.

Although $[R]_\infty$ may be zero nevertheless R is produced from the reaction of O. Fig. 3.19 shows plots of j against potential for $j_R = 0$, for $j_R = j_O$ and for $j_R = 2j_O$. Only one sigmoid curve or 'wave' is seen as opposed to the two waves in the irreversible case. Therefore the half-wave potential has to be defined as the half-way point on the overall wave. The total height of the wave is $(j_O + j_R)$ and the half-wave point is observed when

$$j_{\frac{1}{2}} = \tfrac{1}{2}(j_O + j_R) - j_R = \tfrac{1}{2}(j_O - j_R).$$

Now put $\theta' = O$ in (3.30) and we also obtain

$$j = \tfrac{1}{2}(j_O - j_R).$$

Hence for the reversible case†

$$E_{\frac{1}{2}} = E^{\ominus}. \tag{3.31}$$

The concentration profiles at $\theta' = 0$ are shown in Fig. 3.19. It may be seen that in keeping with the equilibrium requirement, whatever the concentration ratio in the bulk of the solution, at the electrode and at a potential of $E^{\ominus}$,

$$[O]_* = [R]_*.$$

Measurement of e.m.f.s of cells

The full equation (3.25) tells us that $j = 0$ when

$$\frac{j_O}{j_R} = \exp(2\theta')$$

or

$$\frac{[O]_\infty}{[R]_\infty} = \exp\left[\frac{F(E - E^{\ominus})}{RT}\right]$$

which is the Nernst equation. This applies both to the reversible and irreversible cases. But in fact the measurements of e.m.f.s at a redox electrode will be upset by the presence in the solution of other electroactive impurities, such as dissolved oxygen or Cu^{2+} from the still. At the potential we are trying to measure, these impurities may well be reacting on the electrode. Hence we will write j_{Im} for a flux of impurities; assuming that each molecule of impurity reacts with n_{Im} electrons, the observed current will be:

$$i = FA(j + n_{Im}j_{Im}).$$

---

† This equality is only strictly correct when the diffusion coefficients of O and R are equal. For many systems this is a good approximation. For nearly all reversible systems it will be true that

$$E_{\frac{1}{2}} \approx E^{\ominus}.$$

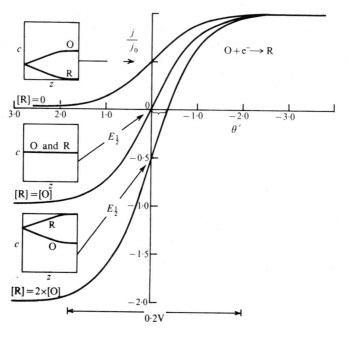

FIG. 3.19. Family of reversible current–voltage curves. Each curve is labelled with [R]. Note that $E_{\frac{1}{2}}$ for each curve is at $\theta' = 0$ or $E = E^{\ominus}$; insets show concentration profiles and how equilibrium is maintained at the electrode since at $E^{\ominus}, [O]_* = [R]_*$. The distance $\smile$ on the x-axis agrees with the Nernst equation.

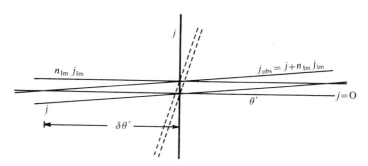

FIG. 3.20. The effect of electrode kinetics on the measurement of e.m.f.s. For an irreversible system the flux due to an impurity causes a large shift in the point where $i = 0$. For a reversible system (broken lines) the shift is much smaller.

Hence as shown in Fig. 3.20 when $i = 0$

$$j = -n_{Im}j_{Im}$$

and the error in the potential is given by

$$\delta\theta' = \frac{F\delta E}{RT} \simeq -\frac{n_{Im}j_{Im}}{(\partial j/\partial\theta')_{j=0}}$$

$$= n_I\left[\frac{[Im]_\infty}{[O]_\infty} + \frac{[Im]_\infty}{[R]_\infty} + \frac{1}{2}\frac{k'_D}{k'_0}\frac{[Im]_\infty}{\sqrt{([O]_\infty[R]_\infty)}}\right].$$

Now it is to be hoped that $[Im]_\infty \ll$ both $[O]_\infty$ and $[R]_\infty$, but the third term can still interfere if $k'_D \gg k'_0$. Thus the kinetic condition for the successful measurement of e.m.f.s is that

$$\frac{k'_D}{k'_0}\frac{[Im]_\infty}{\sqrt{([O]_\infty[R]_\infty)}} \ll 1. \tag{3.32}$$

Indeed for an irreversible system the potential of zero current can wander between the two irreversible waves (see Fig. 3.17). The separation of these waves will be larger the slower the kinetics (see Fig. 3.18) and this large separation will lead to even larger variations in the potential of zero current. Since the kinetic barrier is large at the electrode it is not surprising that nonsense will be obtained if one attempts to measure a thermodynamic quantity. On the other hand the faster the kinetics the more accurate will be the measurement of the e.m.f. and the less it will be affected by impurities. All the familiar systems of classical electrochemistry, such as H^+/H_2, Br_2/Br^-, $Fe(III)/Fe(II)$, have fast electrode kinetics. But stick an electrode in a solution containing alcohol and the corresponding aldehyde and one cannot (unfortunately) measure the $E^\ominus$ because the kinetics of the electrode reaction are too slow.

Comparison of reversible and irreversible systems

We can therefore summarize the differences between reversible and irreversible systems:

	Reversible $k'_0 \gg k'_D$	Irreversible $k'_0 \ll k'_D$
Near $E = E^\ominus$	$O_* \rightleftarrows R_*$ In equilibrium	$[O]_* \approx [O]_\infty$ $[R]_* \approx [R]_\infty$
Current–voltage curve	One wave	Two waves
$E_{\frac{1}{2}}$	$E_{\frac{1}{2}} = E^\ominus$	$E_{\frac{1}{2}} = E^\ominus \pm \ln\left(\frac{k'_D}{k'_0}\right)$
e.m.f. measurements	O.K. unless $[O]_\infty$ or $[R]_\infty \sim [Im]_\infty$	$[Im]_\infty \ll \frac{k'_0}{k'_D}\sqrt{([O]_\infty[R]_\infty)}$ $\ll \sqrt{([O]_\infty[R]_\infty)}$

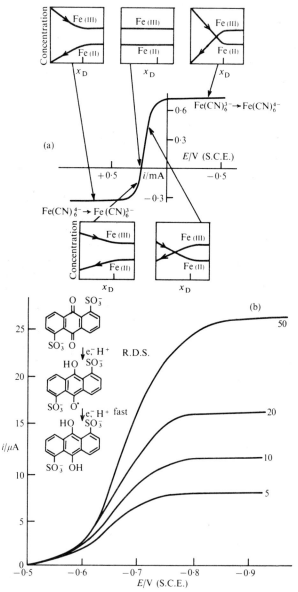

FIG. 3.21. Typical experimental current–voltage curves on a R.D.E. A is a reversible system, $Fe(CN)_6^{3-}/Fe(CN)_6^{4-}$; the insets show the concentration profiles. B is an irreversible system, the reduction of 1,5-anthraquinone disulphonate; the numbers describe the rotation speed of the electrode in Hz. Data measured in the author's laboratory by M. L. Hitchman and A. H. Davis.

Fig. 3.21 presents experimental results on a rotating disc electrode for a typical reversible system:

$$Fe(CN)_6^{3-} + e^- \rightleftharpoons Fe(CN)_6^{4-}$$

and an irreversible system at different rotation speeds:

Their similarity to the theoretical curves is intended to be apparent.

The dropping mercury electrode

The dropping mercury electrode (D.M.E.) that was developed by Heyrovsky and the Czech school preceded the R.D.E. by several decades. As a result it has been more widely used. However, it is a more complicated system than the R.D.E. With the R.D.E. we can set up a genuine steady state in which concentrations and currents do not vary with time. With the D.M.E. this is not the case. Instead there is a cyclical pattern in which concentration varies with both time and distance.

The apparatus is drawn in Fig. 3.22 and a strip cartoon of its operation in Fig. 3.23. The cyclic system renews the region round the drop with fresh solution when the drop falls off. The diffusion gradients around the drop are always steep and do not spread far out into the solution. Hence the horrors of the Albery equation (3.1) are avoided. The theoretical description of this system will be presented in a simplified fashion.

We start by considering the spreading out of the concentration gradients from the surface of the drop as usual measured with a distance x normal to the electrode surface. Because the radius of the drop is considerably greater than the thickness of the diffusion layer we treat the drop as a plane surface as shown in Fig. 3.24.

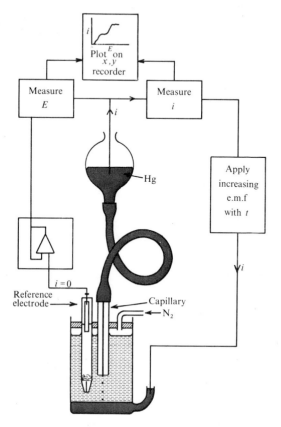

FIG. 3.22. The dropping mercury electrode set up for polarography. Δ is an operational amplifier which ensures that no current passes through the reference electrode. N_2 is passed over the solution to remove O_2 which is electroactive.

We will calculate the current for the transport-limited case that is when the electrode is very active and $c = 0$ at $x = 0$. Fick's Second Law gives us (see Fig. 3.6)

$$\frac{\partial c}{\partial t} = D\frac{\partial^2 c}{\partial x^2}. \tag{3.33}$$

This equation has boundary conditions:

$t = 0$	$c = c_\infty$	fresh solution
$x \to \infty$	$c = c_\infty$	bulk solution
$x = 0$	$c = 0$	active electrode.

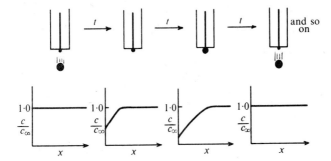

FIG. 3.23. Cyclical operation of the dropping mercury electrode; x is the distance from the mercury surface.

The solution to this equation and its boundary conditions is:

$$c = \frac{2c_\infty}{\sqrt{\pi}} \int_0^{x/2\sqrt{(Dt)}} \exp(-\lambda^2)\,d\lambda = c_\infty \, \mathrm{erf}\left(\frac{x}{2\sqrt{(Dt)}}\right). \qquad (3.34)$$

The magic letters erf standing for *error function* are a posh way of writing the integral. Appendix (5) shows that this equation is the correct solution.

From (3.34) or (10.1) in Appendix (5)

$$\left(\frac{\partial c}{\partial x}\right)_0 = \frac{c_\infty}{\sqrt{(\pi D t)}}.$$

If we follow the same procedure for the R.D.E. and write

$$\left(\frac{\partial c}{\partial x}\right)_0 = \frac{c_\infty}{x_D(t)}$$

we obtain

$$x_D(t) = \sqrt{(\pi \dot{D} t)}.$$

Thus the diffusion thickness is a function of time and increases with $t^{\frac{1}{2}}$. In using the D.M.E. one makes one's measurements just before the drop falls

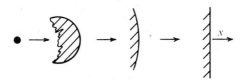

FIG. 3.24. For a thin layer, the curvature of the drop is insignificant and it can be treated as a plane.

off; that is at $t = t_D$ where t_D is the drop time. We will then define a special value of x_D, the thickness of the diffusion layer as the drop falls off

$$x_{D,D} = x_D(t_D) = \sqrt{(\pi D t_D)}.$$ (3.35)

For a typical value of $t_D \sim 3\,\text{s}$, $x_{D,D} \sim 0.1\,\text{mm}$. This is at least an order of magnitude smaller than r the radius of the drop since $r \sim 1\,\text{mm}$, and so the approximation in Fig. 3.24 is justified.

Substituting for $x_{D,D}$ in (3.34)

$$\frac{c}{c_\infty} = \text{erf}\left\{\frac{\sqrt{\pi}}{2}\sqrt{\left(\frac{t_D}{t}\right)}\frac{x}{x_{D,D}}\right\}.$$ (3.36)

Fig. 3.25 shows plots of c/c_∞ versus $x/x_{D,D}$ for different values of t/t_D.

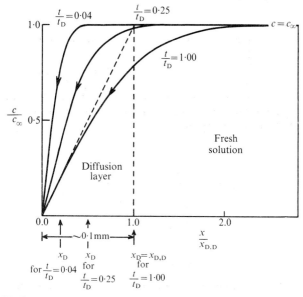

FIG. 3.25. Concentration profiles from eqn (3.36) for a limiting current at a D.M.E. at different times in the growth of the drop. Note that when the drop falls off ($t/t_D = 1.00$), the concentration gradient at the electrode is given by $c_\infty/x_{D,D}$. The spreading out of the diffusion layer is also indicated.

Now the current to the drop electrode is

$$i = nFAD\left(\frac{\partial c}{\partial x}\right)_0 = nF4\pi r^2 D\frac{c_\infty}{x_D}.$$

In this equation the surface area is continually increasing because of the growth of the drops. The flow of the mercury through the capillary is constant.

Let this be m'_{Hg} kg s^{-1}. Then the volume is given by:

$$\tfrac{4}{3}\pi r^3 = \frac{m'_{Hg}}{\rho_{Hg}}t$$

or

$$r = \left(\frac{3m'_{Hg}t}{4\pi\rho_{Hg}}\right)^{\frac{1}{3}}.$$

Hence

$$i = nF(36\pi)^{\frac{1}{3}}\left(\frac{m'_{Hg}}{\rho_{Hg}}\right)^{\frac{2}{3}}\sqrt{\left(\frac{D}{\pi}\right)}t^{\frac{1}{6}}c_\infty\cdot\sqrt{\left(\frac{7}{3}\right)}$$

$$= 4\cdot16nF\left(\frac{m'_{Hg}}{\rho_{Hg}}\right)^{\frac{2}{3}}\sqrt{D}t^{\frac{1}{6}}c_\infty. \tag{3.37}$$

The mysterious factor of $\sqrt{(7/3)}$ arises because in our simplified treatment we have ignored the fact that the expansion of the spherical drop moves the electrode surface closer to the fresh solution and thus the layers do not become quite so depleted as our treatment suggests. Eqn (3.37) is the *Ilkovic equation*. It predicts that the current rises to the power of $t^{\frac{1}{6}}$ giving the saw-tooth pattern shown in Fig. 3.26. The $t^{\frac{1}{6}}$ term describes the balance between the increasing area of the drop and the declining flux per unit area. At the end of each drop the current is largest and di/dt is smallest and that is why measurements are made at this point in the cycle. Hence at the end of each drop the D.M.E. has a reasonably well-defined diffusion layer given by eqn (3.37).

We can therefore define as before

$$k'_D = \frac{D}{x_{D,D}}$$

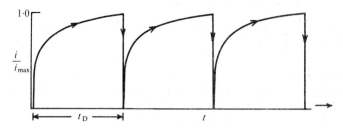

FIG. 3.26. Variation of current with time at a D.M.E. according to eqn (3.37). The current per unit area decreases (see Fig. 3.25) but the increasing area leads to a net increase in current.

and to a good approximation the previous analysis of current voltage curves at the R.D.E. will then apply with this value of $x_{D,D}$. The simplified theory has not dealt with the following complications:

1. The drop is spherical and the planar diffusion equation is not strictly correct,
2. x_D has been calculated for the limiting current and not with the correct general boundary condition

$$D\left(\frac{\partial c}{\partial x}\right) = k'c_*,$$

3. The drop is not a perfect sphere because it is attached to the capillary,
4. Because the drop surface is expanding all the time there is a contribution to the current from charging the increasing double-layer capacitance.

Comparison of R.D.E. and D.M.E.

Because of their importance in the study of electrode kinetics we now present a comparison of the rotating disc and dropping mercury electrodes.

Advantages of R.D.E. compared to D.M.E.

1. It can be made of any metal (one can even make rotating Hg disc electrodes). Hg cannot be used at potentials more positive than 0·2 V with respect to the saturated calomel electrode since it starts dissolving.
2. Genuine steady state is established so there are no effects from double layer charging.
3. Theory is simpler and more accurate.
4. Rotation speed is a more convenient experimental variable to control x_D, than the drop time.
5. $(k'_D)_{RDE} > (k'_D)_{DME}$ so that faster electrode kinetics can be studied.

Advantages of D.M.E. compared to R.D.E.

1. The electrode surface is continually renewed with fresh clean mercury and so does not become poisoned; and, being a liquid, it is more reproducible.
2. H_3O^+ and H_2O do not react easily on a Hg surface.
3. Heyrovsky won the Nobel prize.

Polarography

Traditionally polarography has been carried out on a dropping mercury electrode, but the technique can be used with any electrode system that has a fixed x_D or k'_D. The potential of an electrode is varied linearly with time. The different electroactive species in the solution have different values of $E_{\frac{1}{2}}$. As the potential sweeps through the $E_{\frac{1}{2}}$ of a species, the current rises steeply giving a 'wave'. For a reversible system the change is from driving the system in one direction,

$$R \rightarrow O + e^-$$

to driving it in the opposite one

$$O + e^- \rightarrow R.$$

For an irreversible system the species either changes from being electroactive to being inert,

$$R \rightarrow O + e^- \quad \text{to nothing,}$$

or vice versa,

$$\text{nothing to} \quad O + e^- \rightarrow R.$$

The height of the wave is proportional to $[O]_\infty + [R]_\infty$ for a reversible system and to $[O]_\infty$ or $[R]_\infty$ for an irreversible system. The half wave potential of a reversible sysem (3.31) does not alter with the electrode system and can be used to identify the species involved. For an irreversible wave $E_{\frac{1}{2}}$ depends upon k'_D, but if k'_D is known or if it is kept constant and the system is calibrated, $E_{\frac{1}{2}}$ can be used in the same way. It might seem strange that for the irreversible system one can obtain both $[O]_\infty$ and $[R]_\infty$ while for the reversible system one only obtains $([O]_\infty + [R]_\infty)$. But with the reversible system one can find the extra piece of information by measuring the e.m.f. when $i = 0$; this gives from the Nernst equation the ratio of $[O]_\infty/[R]_\infty$. The range of the potential sweep is limited by one of these factors:

1. The decomposition of the solvent, e.g.

$$H_2O + e^- \rightarrow \tfrac{1}{2}H_2 + OH^-$$

or

$$H_2O \rightarrow \tfrac{1}{2}O_2 + 2H^+ + 2e^-.$$

2. The decomposition of some other species present in large concentrations ($\sim 1 \text{ mol m}^{-3}$), e.g. H^+.
3. The dissolution of the metal (e.g. Hg) and its loss into the solution

$$M \rightarrow M^{n+} + ne^-.$$

Fig. 3.27 shows a typical polarogram obtained on a Hg drop electrode. Since

$$i_L = nFAD\frac{[X]_\infty}{x_D} \tag{3.38}$$

and since i_L can be measured when it is as low as 1 μA the method can be used for concentrations as low as 10^{-3} mol m^{-3} (or 1 μM) where we have taken in (3.38) $n = 1$, $A = 100 \text{ mm}^2$, $D = 1 \text{ m}^2\text{G s}^{-1}$, and $x_D = 10 \text{ }\mu\text{m}$.

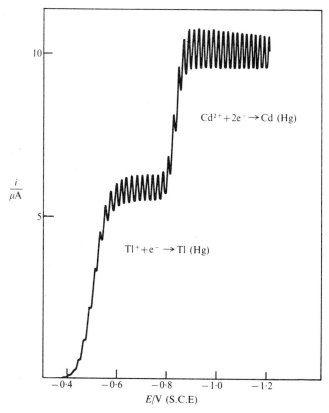

Fig. 3.27. Typical polarogram at a D.M.E. for the reduction of Tl^+ and Cd^{2+}. Data from the author's laboratory.

Electrode kinetics and steady-state methods

Since the current–voltage curve for reversible systems does not depend on k'_0, we cannot study electrode kinetics by the steady-state method for these systems. This is because the electrode reaction is not the rate-determining step. On the other hand for irreversible systems we can use (3.17) or (3.20) and rearrange it to obtain:

$$\frac{1}{j} - \frac{1}{j_L} = \frac{1}{k'_1[O]_\infty} = \frac{\exp(\alpha EF/RT)}{k'_{E=0}[O]_\infty} = \frac{\exp(\alpha E'F/RT)}{k'[O]_\infty}.$$

The $(j_L)^{-1}$ term corrects for the variation in concentration in the diffusion layer. Using $i = nFAj$ we obtain for a reduction:

$$-\ln\left[\frac{1}{i}-\frac{1}{i_L}\right] = -\frac{\alpha EF}{RT}+\ln(k_1')_{E=0}+\ln[O]_\infty+\ln(nFA) \qquad (3.39)$$

$$= \ln(i_c) = -\frac{\alpha EF}{RT}+\frac{\alpha E^\ominus F}{RT}+\ln k_0'+\ln[O]_\infty+\ln(nFA). \qquad (3.40)$$

For an oxidation we obtain by a similar argument

$$-\ln\left[\frac{1}{i}-\frac{1}{i_L}\right] = \frac{\beta EF}{RT}+\ln(k_{-1}')_{E=0}+\ln[R]_\infty+\ln(nFA) \qquad (3.41)$$

$$= \ln i_c = \frac{\beta EF}{RT}-\frac{\beta E^\ominus F}{RT}+\ln k_0'+\ln[R]_\infty+\ln(nFA). \qquad (3.42)$$

Since $|i_L| = nFAk_D'[O \text{ or } R]_\infty$, another form of (3.39) is:

$$\ln(i_c/i_L) = \ln(k_1')_{E=0}-\ln k_D'-\frac{\alpha EF}{RT} \qquad (3.43)$$

and for the oxidation replace α with $(-\beta)$. In these equations we have defined a current corrected for concentration polarization.

From (3.39) to (3.42) the Tafel plots are obtained by plotting $\ln i_c$ against E. For irreversible systems, as discussed above, the reverse reaction is unimportant. So the Tafel plot of the corrected current i_c against potential should hold, not just for a limited range of potential as in Fig. 3.16, but for the whole of the wave. Fig. 3.28 shows the data for the anthraquinone current–voltage curve (at $W = 50$ Hz) in Fig. 3.21 plotted in this way. A linear Tafel plot is found for the whole of the wave for which $\alpha = 0.48$ showing that the first electron transfer is the rate determining step. Similarly the order of the reaction can be found by plotting *at constant potential* $\ln i_c$ against $\ln[O \text{ or } R]_\infty$. In this case the answer would be a gradient of 1 since we have taken a first-order example. This is the most common type of reaction.

For higher-order reactions more complicated algebra is needed. However, one can calculate the surface concentrations from eqn (3.18) and knowing k_D' the problem can be solved.

For a single-electron transfer where $n = 1$ we have the particular relation that

$$\alpha+\beta = 1.$$

This does not hold for multistep reactions. For single electron transfers one can find the thermodynamic quantity $E^\ominus$ by extrapolating the Tafel plots until they intersect. This is equivalent to measuring an equilibrium constant from the ratio of the forward and backward rate constants. Fig. 3.29 shows plots

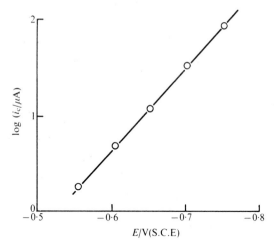

FIG. 3.28. Tafel plot of current corrected for concentration polarization according to eqn (3.40). Data are from the 50 Hz current–voltage curve in Fig. 3.21.

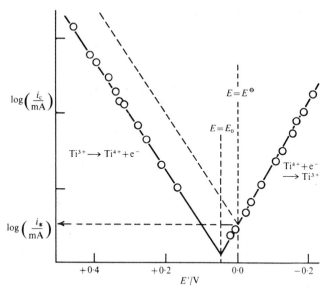

FIG. 3.29. Essin's data for Ti^{4+}/Ti^{3+} system in 2 mol dm^{-3} H_2SO_4 plotted according to eqn (3.40) and eqn (3.42); $E' = E - E^{\ominus}$, $[Ti^{4+}]/[Ti^{3+}] = 5\cdot7$ and the separation ↔ corresponds to $(RT/F) \ln 5\cdot7$. The dashed line shows the oxidation current that would have been observed for $5\cdot7 \times$ (more Ti^{3+} so that $[Ti^{3+}] = [Ti^{4+}]$).

for the Ti^{4+}/Ti^{3+} system investigated by Essin. Using (3.40) and (3.42) we find that the lines intersect when

$$-\frac{\alpha EF}{RT}+\frac{\alpha E^{\ominus}F}{RT}+\ln\,[O]_{\infty} = \frac{\beta EF}{RT}+\frac{\beta E^{\ominus}F}{RT}+\ln\,[R]_{\infty}$$

or when

$$E = E_0 = E^{\ominus}+\frac{RT}{F}\ln\frac{[O]_x}{[R]_{\infty}}$$

which is our old friend the Nernst equation. This is because when $E = E_0$ no current flows in the particular system under study. For reversible and borderline systems E_0 can be observed directly but for very irreversible systems, as discussed above, E_0 cannot be observed and this extrapolation procedure can then be used. Knowing E_0 and the concentrations, $E^{\ominus}$ can be found. This procedure may not work for multistep reactions (see Chapter 5).

For the results in Fig. 3.29 the ratio $[Ti^{4+}]/[Ti^{3+}] = 5.7$. The dashed line shows the current that would have been observed if 5·7 times more Ti^{3+} had been used so that the concentrations were equal. For these particular conditions $E_0 = E^{\ominus}$. From (3.40) or (3.42) the value i_* of i_c at this point is given by

$$\log i_* = \log k'_0 + \log\,[O\ or\ R]_{\infty} - \log(nFA). \tag{3.44}$$

In this equation the only unknown is k'_0 and hence its value can be found. It can also be found from the intercepts of single Tafel plots of either (3.40) or (3.42) as long as a value of $E^{\ominus}$ can be measured or calculated. For more complicated mechanisms one should use eqns (3.39) and (3.41) to measure individual rate constants at some standard potential.

Limits on size of i

Despite the sensitivity of the current to variations in potential the range over which measurements of i can be made is restricted. First, the current must be large enough to distinguish from the 'noise'. In normal practice this means that the current must be larger than 1 μA. Modern techniques of data acquisition can, however, lower this limit to 1 nA. Secondly the current must be significantly less than the limiting current, which is usually of the order of 1 mA. Thus even without special techniques currents can be measured through three to four orders of magnitude.

Potential step on a stationary electrode

The simplest method for studying electrochemical kinetics is the steady-state method on the R.D.E. since then we have only to consider the variation of concentration with distance. The disadvantage of the technique however is that if the reaction is too fast and the system is reversible the current is not determined by the electrode kinetics. For these systems other methods have to be used. An obvious way to convert the reversible condition $k'_0 \gg k'_D$ into the irreversible condition $k'_0 \ll k'_D$ is to increase k'_D. Now if we suddenly jump the potential of a stationary electrode from that potential at which no current flows, which we shall call E_0, to a preset value then the problem is almost the same and has the same boundary conditions at $t = 0$ and as $x \to \infty$ as (3.33). For the D.M.E. the start is the growth of a drop; for the present case it is the sudden shift in potential. The situation is sketched in Fig. 3.30. At short times x_D is small and k'_D is therefore large, so that faster electrode kinetics can be observed.

Life and this book are too short for the complete mathematical description of this situation; we will consider the following special case and use the

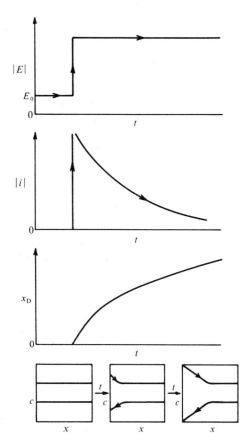

FIG. 3.30. Variation with time of potential, current, diffusion thickness and concentration profiles for potential step technique.

methods we have developed so far. We will assume that the displacement of the potential from E_0 is not too large (~ 5 mV) and that we are interested in a mathematical description at short times. From eqn (3.23) the diffusion thickness is given by

$$x_D = \sqrt{(\pi D t)}$$

and

$$k'_D = \sqrt{\frac{D}{\pi t}}.$$

Hence at short times k'_D is large and this is what we want in order to observe the fast electrode kinetics.

When k'_D is large and if the displacement is small the surface concentrations $[O]_*$ and $[R]_*$ do not change greatly. Hence we can write as for the steady-state case from eqn (3.21)

$$j \approx \frac{k'_1[O]_\infty - k'_{-1}[R]_\infty}{1 + (k'_1 + k'_{-1})/k'_D}. \tag{3.45}$$

This case is not a genuine steady state and (3.45) will only hold when $[O]_* \approx [O]_\infty$ and $[R]_* \approx [R]_\infty$. These are their values at $t = 0$ since at that time the system is unperturbed. Substituting for k'_D and writing $(1 + \lambda)^{-1} \approx 1 - \lambda$ when λ is small we obtain

$$j \approx (k'_1[O]_\infty - k'_{-1}[R]_\infty)\left(1 - \sqrt{\pi}\frac{k'_1 + k'_{-1}}{\sqrt{D}}\sqrt{t}\right). \tag{3.46}$$

This approximation may be compared with the full treatment which gives:

$$j \simeq (k'_1[O]_\infty - k'_{-1}[R]_\infty)\left(1 - \frac{2}{\sqrt{\pi}}\frac{k'_1 + k'_{-1}}{\sqrt{D}}\sqrt{t}\right). \tag{3.47}$$

The two expressions differ only in the numerical constant of $\sqrt{\pi}$ and $2/\sqrt{\pi}$ in the small term. By measuring the current as a function of time and plotting it against $\sqrt{t}$ one can extrapolate back to zero time and hence obtain values of

$$j_0 = k'_1[O]_\infty - k'_{-1}[R]_\infty.$$

This is shown in Fig. 3.31.

Since one has to catch the system before the concentration polarization has set in, the currents must be recorded on an oscilloscope. Writing in the potential dependence of k'_1 and k'_{-1} we have

$$j_0 = k'_0 \left\{ \exp\left[\frac{-\alpha F(E - E^\ominus)}{RT}\right][O]_\infty - \exp\left[\frac{\beta F(E - E^\ominus)}{RT}\right][R]_\infty \right\} \tag{3.48}$$

where

$$\alpha + \beta = n \tag{3.49}$$

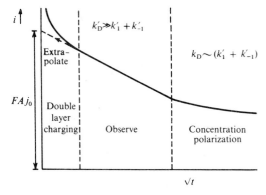

FIG. 3.31. Potential step technique and the extrapolation according to (3.47) against t to remove the effects of concentration polarization.

and we have generated the equation of an n-electron transfer.

The Nernst equation gives us

$$\exp \frac{-\alpha F(E_0 - E^{\ominus})}{RT} = \left(\frac{[R]_\infty}{[O]_\infty}\right)^{\alpha/n} \tag{3.50}$$

where E_0 is the potential for which $j = 0$. We now define the *over-potential* E_η where

$$E_\eta = E - E_0. \tag{3.51}$$

The over-potential measures the displacement of the potential from the point where no current flows. (Electrochemists often write this as η but to others this denotes viscosity.) Substituting eqns (3.49)–(3.51) in eqn (3.48) we obtain

$$j_0 = k'_0 [O]_\infty^{\beta/n} [R]_\infty^{\alpha/n} \left\{ \exp\left(-\frac{\alpha F E_\eta}{RT}\right) - \exp\left(\frac{\beta F E_\eta}{RT}\right) \right\}. \tag{3.52}$$

Now we only make a small displacement in the potential from E_0 and hence $E_\eta \ll F/RT$ and the exponentials can be expanded to give:

$$j_0 = -k'_0 [O]_\infty^{\beta/n} [R]_\infty^{\alpha/n} \frac{nFE_\eta}{RT}. \tag{3.53}$$

Values of j_0 at a fixed value of E_η and $[O]_\infty$ with varying $[R]_\infty$ allow a determination of α from a plot of $\ln j_0$ against $\ln [R]_\infty$. Once α is known k'_0 can be calculated from (3.53). Note also that when $[O]_\infty = [R]_\infty$ the calculation of k'_0 does not require α, since

$$\alpha/n + \beta/n = 1.$$

This method cannot be used for irreversible systems since for low values of k'_0 and FE_n/RT, j_0 would be too small. Not enough material would react. Hence the different techniques are complementary:

R.D.E.	D.M.E.	Potential step
$t \to \infty$	$t = t_D$	$t \to 0$
Steady state	Cyclic	Single shot
Concentration polarization established and calculated	Concentration polarization established and calculated	Extrapolate to remove effects of concentration polarization
$k'_0 < 10^{-4}\ \mathrm{m\ s^{-1}}$	$k'_0 < 10^{-6}\ \mathrm{m\ s^{-1}}$	$10^{-5} < k'_0 < 10^{-3}\ \mathrm{m\ s^{-1}}$

The limit of $k'_0 < 10^{-3}\ \mathrm{m\ s^{-1}}$ for the potential step arises from the fact that the double layer has to be charged before useful results can be obtained. The charging of the double layer by the potential step is like applying a voltage step to:

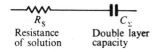

R_s
Resistance
of solution

C_Σ
Double layer
capacity

It takes 10^{-5} to 10^{-4} s for this to happen and while the charging current is passing it is impossible to distinguish between it and the current from the electrode kinetics. With more sophisticated control of the potential an extra pulse of current can be provided at the start to charge the double layer, and then faster rate constants can be measured.

Faradaic impedance methods

Another class of methods to measure fast reactions developed by Randles, Gerischer, and Sluyters amongst others is to use alternating current. To measure the conductivity of an electrolyte one uses a Wheatstone bridge together with high frequency a.c., in order 'to prevent electrolysis'. Under these conditions the circuit in the cell can be imagined to be

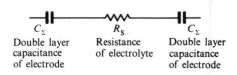

C_Σ
Double layer
capacitance
of electrode

R_s
Resistance
of electrolyte

C_Σ
Double layer
capacitance
of electrode

It can be seen how crucial the double layer capacitance is to the measurement of conductivity. Without it (and without electrolysis) one would have a circuit of the form

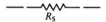

$$R_S$$

which would register an infinite impedance! The more accurate type of conductivity bridge allows one to balance out both the capacity and the resistance of the cell as shown in Fig. 3.32. When the bridge is perfectly balanced the variable components in the bridge R_B and C_B match the R and C of the cell. To study electrode kinetics the d.c. source is added so that the potential across the cell can be adjusted. The cell now behaves as a more complicated circuit since electrolysis not only can but is intended to take place at the electrodes. First of all the impedance of the counter-electrode is negligible since it is much larger than the working electrode. Secondly the resistance of the solution is much smaller than in the typical conductivity experiment because of the added inert salt. Thirdly, there is the *Faradaic impedance* at the working electrode; this arises from the electrochemical reaction taking place there.

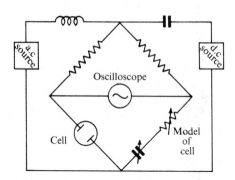

FIG. 3.32. Circuit for measurement of Faradaic impedance. The choke and the capacitance on the top line allow the passage of d.c. and a.c. respectively.

It is neither a resistance nor a capacitance but has its own current–voltage characteristics. However, to simplify the algebra we will assume that it behaves like a resistance. This is not strictly true since the variation in concentration at the electrode surface will cause a shift in the phase of the current with respect to that of the voltage. At high frequencies and for fast electrode reactions however this feature is less important. With this approximation the circuit for the cell now looks like:

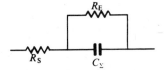

The kinetic information is contained in the size of the resistance R_E. If the electrochemical reactions are fast then R_E will be small; if they are slow then it will be large. By applying an alternating potential to the electrode network at different frequencies we can analyse the different components of the network and hence measure R_E. Let the applied alternating potential be

$$E = E_m \cos(\omega't) \tag{3.54}$$

where E_m is the amplitude and ω' is the frequency.

Then the current through the network is given by

$$i = \frac{E_m}{(R_X^2 + R_Y^2)}[R_X \cos(\omega't) - R_Y \sin(\omega't)], \tag{3.55}$$

where

$$R_X = R_S + \frac{R_E}{1 + (\omega'C_\Sigma R_E)^2} \tag{3.56}$$

and

$$R_Y = \frac{\omega'C_\Sigma R_E^2}{1 + (\omega'C_\Sigma R_E)^2}. \tag{3.57}$$

These relations are derived in Appendix 6. Note that the current contains a sine term as well as a cosine. This means that it is not *in phase* with the voltage since (3.54) only contains a cosine; the current reaches its maximum at a different time to the voltage (see Fig. 3.33).

The R_X term in eqn (3.55) describes the component of the current that is in phase with the alternating potential in eqn (3.54). The R_Y term describes the component of the current that is 90° out of phase with the applied potential. Notice that when

$$\omega' \to 0, \qquad R_X \to R_S + R_E \quad \text{and} \quad R_Y \to 0.$$

At low frequency the capacitance has a large impedance and the network behaves as a pure resistance of $(R_S + R_E)$. On the other hand when

$$\omega' \to \infty, \qquad R_X \to R_S \quad \text{and} \quad R_Y \to 0.$$

At high frequency the capacitance has a low impedance. Again the network behaves as a pure resistance but with the smaller value of R_S. At intermediate frequencies R_Y is not zero and there will be an out of phase component as the

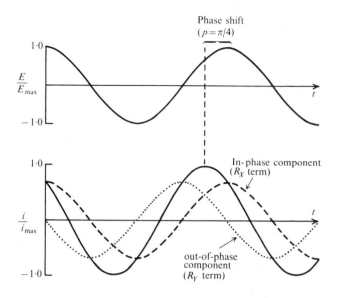

Fig. 3.33. Because of the double layer capacity the current is out of phase with the voltage. It can be expressed as the sum of an in-phase and an out-of-phase component. The particular case illustrated is for $R_Y = R_X$ in eqn (3.55).

capacitance charges and discharges. One method to measure R_X and R_Y is to balance them on a Wheatstone bridge against the network shown in Fig. 3.32:

$$\begin{array}{cc} \underset{R_B}{\wedge\!\wedge\!\wedge} & \underset{C_B}{\dashv\vdash} \end{array}$$

For the bridge components letting $R_E \to \infty$ in (3.56) and (3.57) gives

$$R'_X = R_B \quad \text{and} \quad R'_Y = \frac{1}{\omega' C_B}.$$

When the bridge is balanced with respect to both the in phase and out of phase components then†

$$R_X = R'_X = R_B \quad \text{and} \quad R_Y = R'_Y = 1/\omega' C_B. \tag{3.58}$$

Having measured R_X and R_Y a convenient method of treating the results is to plot a Sluyters diagram† in which at each frequency R_Y is plotted against R_X. As shown in Fig. 3.34, from eqns (3.56) and (3.57), a semi-circle is obtained,

† This type of diagram can be linked to the Argand diagram for complex numbers, see Appendix (6).

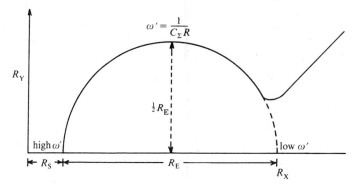

FIG. 3.34. Sluyters diagram of R_Y (out-of-phase component in eqn (3.55)) against R_X (in-phase component). Diameter of semi-circle gives R_E. Simplified theory predicts a semi-circle. Deviation at low frequency caused by variation in surface concentrations.

which goes from the high-frequency limit of R_S to the low-frequency limit of $(R_E + R_S)$; these limits were discussed above. In this simplified treatment we have ignored the effect of concentration changes near the electrode. They will be more important at low frequency and if they are included then the plot of R_Y against R_X will have the shape shown in Fig. 3.34. The diameter of the circle gives the value of R_E. Sluyters has developed other variations of this approach; for instance one can keep the frequency constant and vary the concentrations of the reactants.

Having obtained a value of R_E we can now relate this to the kinetic parameters using eqn (3.53). For small values of E_η compared to F/RT, and for displacements about E_0 the potential at which no current flows,

$$j \simeq -k_0'[O]_\infty^{\beta/n}[R]_\infty^{\alpha/n}\left(\frac{nE_\eta E}{RT}\right).$$

(This is in the linear region of Fig. 3.16.) Therefore

$$R_E = \left|\frac{dE}{di}\right| = \frac{RT}{nAF^2 k_0'[O]_\infty^{\beta/n}[R]_\infty^{\alpha/n}}.$$

By determining R_E as a function of $[R]_\infty$ or $[O]_\infty$, α can be found and then k_0'. As one might expect the larger is k_0' the smaller is R_E.

Some typical results from the a.c. method are shown in Fig. 3.35. They were obtained by Cooper and Parsons for the reaction $Br^- \rightleftarrows Br\cdot + e^-$, which is the rate determining step in the Br_2/Br^- system.

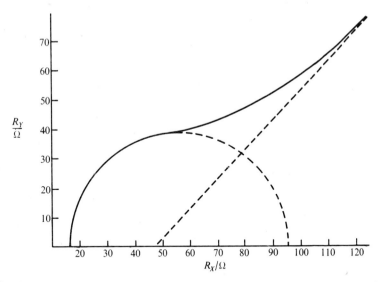

FIG. 3.35. Results for the Br_2/Br^- system showing the impedance characteristics of the rate determining step

$$Br^- \rightleftharpoons Br^-_{ads} + e^-.$$

(Data from Cooper and Parsons.)

Comparison of methods

We have discussed three methods of measuring electrochemical kinetics, the steady state, the potential step, and Faradaic impedance. There are many other techniques; for instance one can control the current and measure the variation of potential with time. The methods selected are among the more important and they also can be compared with techniques used in homogeneous kinetics. The steady state method in electrochemistry is similar to classical methods in ordinary kinetics except that the concentration varies with distance rather than time. The potential step to measure faster reactions is similar to the temperature jump method developed by Eigen for the study of fast homogeneous reactions in solution;† a step function is applied to the system and the system's response is measured. Besides perturbing the system with a step function one can perturb it periodically. In homogeneous kinetics this is done by using ultrasonics; in electrochemical kinetics by applying an

† See Bradley's *Fast reactions* (OCS 23).

alternating potential at the electrode. So we can make the following comparisons:

	Homogeneous	Electrochemical
Slow reactions	Variation of c with t is measured; c does not vary with x	Variation of c with x is measured; c does not vary with t (for R.D.E.)
Fast reactions	Step function, e.g. T Jump	Potential step
	Ultrasonics	Alternating current.

The electrode as a giant ion

We end this chapter by carrying the comparison between an ion in solution and an electrode a little further. We have discussed three important properties of the electrode: its charge, its reactivity, and the transport of species to and from the electrode. These properties are also important in characterizing the behaviour of an ion in solution and we can summarize the arguments already presented:

	Ion	Electrode
Charge	Fixed for any single ion	Varied by external potentiometer
	Debye–Hückel theory	Double layer theory
Reactivity	Fixed for any single ion	Varied by external potentiometer
	Can be varied systematically in a stepwise fashion, e.g. by replacing C—H with C—Cl	Can be varied continuously
	Brønsted law Hammett relationship	Tafel law
Transport	Fixed for any single ion	Varied by drop height for D.M.E. or by rotation speed for R.D.E.
	Diffusion	Diffusion and convection

The great difference is that all three properties of the electrode are under control and can be varied externally. The electrode is a single giant species; as long as it has a wire sticking in its back, you can tell it what to do.

4. Single electron transfer reactions

Introduction

RESULTS from kinetic measurements can be used in two different ways. First they can be used to elucidate the mechanism of a reaction and to find out the route by which chemical change takes place. Or secondly, they can be used to study elementary processes in detail and to build up a satisfactory description of the individual steps by which more complicated reactions take place. This chapter deals with the detailed interpretation of single electron transfers; the investigation of more complicated mechanisms is the material of Chapter 5.

After a preliminary description of single electron transfers the chapter starts with the derivation of an expression for the rate constant of a reaction, which is similar to that of absolute reaction rate theory, but which is more satisfactory both on general grounds and also for the particular case of electron transfers. The role of free energy is discussed and the Tafel law is seen to be a linear free-energy relationship. The separation of reactions in solution into several steps each with its own time scale is described and the model is supported by evidence from fluorescence. The importance of tunnelling in electron transfer reactions is emphasized. The role of the solvent (and ligands) in providing the necessary conditions for an isoenergetic electron transfer is next described both qualitatively and semi-quantitatively. The theory predicts a correlation between the rates of homogeneous and electrode electron transfers and that the Tafel plot should be curved. These predictions are compared with experimental data and are found to be in reasonable agreement. The chapter ends with a comparison of electron and proton transfers.

Single electron transfer

The simplest process that can take place at the electrode is the single-electron transfer, for example:

$$Fe(H_2O)_6^{3+} + e^- \rightleftarrows Fe(H_2O)_6^{2+}$$
$$Fe(CN)_6^{3-} + e^- \rightleftarrows Fe(CN)_6^{4-}$$
$$MnO_4^- + e^- \rightleftarrows MnO_4^{2-}$$
$$Eu^{3+} + e^- \rightleftarrows Eu^{2+}$$

In these reactions no bonds are formed or broken. An electron is transferred from or to the electrode. Throughout this chapter the electron-transfer reactions we shall be considering involve no breaking or making of covalent bonds.

Now in Fig. 1.2 the barrier to the reaction was drawn with the same shape as for an ordinary chemical reaction involving for instance H atom transfer. Fig. 4.1 is a traditional picture of the potential energy surface for the reaction:

$$H + H_2 \rightarrow H_2 + H.$$

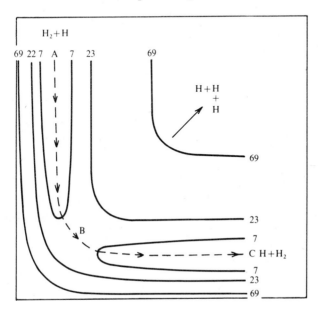

FIG. 4.1. Typical potential energy surface for $H_2 + H \rightarrow H + H_2$. This one was calculated by Porter and Karplus. Energy barrier is obtained along line ABC.

From this surface we derive the type of barrier drawn in Fig. 1.2. This type of barrier is typical for atom-transfer reactions in the gas phase.† But we are dealing with electron-transfer reactions in solution. Both the differences are important. First the low mass of the electron compared to an atom means that quantum-mechanical effects are much more significant. Secondly reactions in solution are multi-molecular, multistep, processes compared to the single activating collision of a simple gas reaction.

The electron-transfer reactions include not only the reactions at an electrode but also outer sphere‡ homogeneous reactions of the type:

$$Ti^{4+} + Fe^{2+} \rightleftarrows Ti^{3+} + Fe^{3+}.$$

† See Pilling (loc. cit.).
‡ Outer-sphere reactions involve no ligand substitution and hence no breaking or making of covalent bonds.

A particular class of this type of reaction is the 'symmetrical' reaction followed by isotopic labelling:

$$Fe^{3+} + Fe^{*2+} \rightleftarrows Fe^{2+} + Fe^{*3+}.$$

In both of the heterogeneous and the homogeneous reactions the first step is a diffusive step. In the homogeneous case this brings the reactants together:

$$Ti^{4+} + Fe^{2+} \rightleftarrows (Ti^{4+}, Fe^{2+}). \tag{4.1}$$

In the electrochemical case it brings the reactant to the electrode

$$(Fe^{3+})_\infty \rightleftarrows (Fe^{3+})_* \tag{4.2}$$

As discussed in eqns (3.16)–(3.20) and in Fig. 3.1 if the subsequent electron transfer is very fast then this diffusive step can be rate determining. But in this chapter we shall not be concerned with diffusion control and so we shall assume that the transport processes are in equilibrium and that it is the electron transfer that is rate determining.

Having got the species into the right place for reaction, we have to change the electronic distribution. This type of process is similar to the electronic transitions that take place when light is absorbed or emitted by a molecule, as shown in Fig. 4.2. The actual movement of the electron cannot be treated classically with the type of surface shown in Fig. 4.1 but has to be treated quantum mechanically. Thus the theory of electron-transfer reactions is connected both with ordinary reaction-rate theory and with the theory describing transitions in electronic spectra. The most recent developments of the

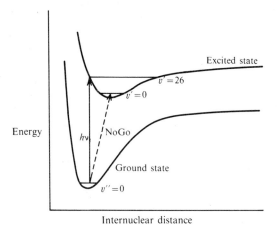

FIG. 4.2. Absorption by I_2 illustrating Franck–Condon principle. There is no time for a change in internuclear distance, while the electron transfer takes place. Data from Mathieson and Rees.

theory have been the work of Marcus, Levich, and Dogonadse, but before describing their work it is important to understand the difference between energy and free energy in determining the rate of a chemical reaction.

The role of free energy

In Fig. 1.2 the vertical axis has been labelled $G^{\ominus}$ rather than U. This is because the reaction does not necessarily take place through the path of lowest possible energy. Just as stable molecules do not spend all their time in the ground state, but because of the thermal energy explore higher energy states, so in a reaction we must not insist that the reacting particles just skim the barrier. Fig. 4.3 shows the final rate-determining process of a reaction for different values of $\Delta S^{\ominus}_{\ddagger}$. In this final process we assume that the reactant molecules are in thermal equilibrium and have a Boltzmann distribution.

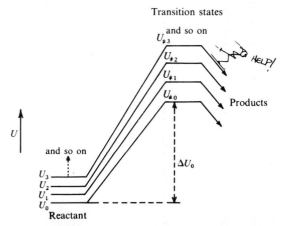

FIG. 4.3. Passage of molecules through a transition state. Each state of the reactant is connected with its particular transition state. During the activation process the degrees of freedom illustrated in the diagram do not have time to become equilibrated and hence there is a one to one (adiabatic) connection.

Rather than assume that the transition state is also in 'equilibrium' with the reactant, a more plausible assumption is that each state of the reactant connects with a state in the transition states as shown by the lines in Fig. 4.3. This has a simple physical reason. For instance if in the reactant a solvent molecule is rotating fast or a CH_3 group is vibrating strongly then these motions will not be quenched in the final process and so the system will move through an appropriate higher state in the transition state. Motion along the reaction coordinate does not affect other motions and therefore the energies of the other motions change adiabatically, since the molecules do not change their states (other than react) we can write very simply that the observed rate will be given by

$$\text{rate} = \sum_i k_i c_i \qquad (4.3)$$

where k_i is the rate constant for the ith level, and c_i is the concentration of species in the ith level. The reactant is in equilibrium between its different energy levels and from the Boltzmann distribution law

$$c_i = \frac{c_\Sigma \exp(-U_i/k_B T)}{q_R} \qquad (4.4)$$

where U_i the energy of the ith level of the reactant is measured from U_0 and q_R is the molecular partition function for the reactant.

The rate constants for the different levels are given by

$$k_i = k_0 \exp[-(U_{\ddagger,i} - U_i)/k_B T] \qquad (4.5)$$

where k_0 is the rate constant for the zeroth level, $U_{\ddagger,i}$ is the energy of the ith level measured from $U_{\ddagger,0}$ and the exponential term describes the different energy of activation that the ith level has compared to the zeroth level.

Substitution of (4.5) and (4.4) in (4.3) gives

$$\text{rate} = c_\Sigma k_0 \frac{\Sigma \exp(-U_{\ddagger,i}/k_B T)}{q_R}$$

$$= c_\Sigma k_0 \frac{q_\ddagger}{q_R} = k_\Sigma c_\Sigma \qquad (4.6)$$

where

$$k_\Sigma = k_0 \frac{q_\ddagger}{q_R}.$$

We can then write

$$k_0 = v_k \exp(-\Delta U_0/k_B T) \qquad (4.7)$$

where v_k is the frequency appropriate to the process that we are studying, and ΔU_0 is the energy difference for the zeroth state. Substitution in (4.6) gives

$$k_\Sigma = v_k \frac{q_\ddagger}{q_R} \exp(-\Delta U_0/k_B T) \qquad (4.8)$$

For a gas reaction v_k would be the collision number. In classical transition-state theory

$$v_k = k_B T/h = 6 \times 10^{12}\ \text{s}^{-1} \qquad (4.9)$$

for $T = 300\ \text{K}$.

With this substitution of (4.9) in (4.8) we then obtain the same answer as transition-state theory. However a more realistic interpretation of v_k may be the frequency of the solvent motion which transfers energy from the solvent lattice to the reactant to enable the change depicted in Fig. 4.3 to take place. In this case, from the dielectric dispersion of water,

$$v_k = v_s \simeq 10^{11}\,\text{s}^{-1}. \tag{4.10}$$

Rearrangement of (4.8) gives

$$\frac{k_\Sigma}{v_k} = \frac{q_\ddagger}{q_R} \exp\left(-\frac{\Delta U_0}{k_B T}\right)$$

$$= \exp\left(-\frac{\Delta G_\ddagger^\ominus}{RT}\right). \tag{4.11}$$

This equation can be thought of as the definition of a free energy of activation, $\Delta G_\ddagger^\ominus$. But also from statistical thermodynamics for an equilibrium†

$$K = \frac{q_P}{q_R} \exp\left(-\frac{\Delta U}{k_B T}\right) \tag{4.12}$$

$$\Delta G_{TD}^\ominus = -RT \ln K$$

and

$$K = \frac{q_P}{q_R}\left[\exp\left(-\frac{\Delta U}{k_B T}\right)\right] = \exp\left(-\frac{\Delta G_{TD}^\ominus}{RT}\right). \tag{4.13}$$

This equation is identical in form with (4.11). Thus $\Delta G_\ddagger^\ominus$ has the same properties as $\Delta G_{TD}^\ominus$, because both of them are related in the same way to a ratio of partition functions $-(q_\ddagger/q_R)$ and (q_P/q_R) respectively. However the derivation of (4.11) has not assumed that the transition state is in 'equilibrium' with the reactant. If $\Delta G_\ddagger^\ominus$ is split up into the entropy and enthalpy terms and if we assume that there is no volume change then

$$\frac{k_\Sigma}{v_k} = \exp\left(-\frac{\Delta H_\ddagger^\ominus}{RT}\right) \exp\left(\frac{\Delta S_\ddagger^\ominus}{R}\right)$$

where

$$\Delta H_\ddagger^\ominus \simeq \Delta U^\ominus$$

and

$$\frac{q_\ddagger}{q_R} = \exp\left(\frac{\Delta S_\ddagger^\ominus}{R}\right).$$

The entropy of activation, $\Delta S_\ddagger^\ominus$, is directly related to the spacing of the levels in the transition state compared to their spacing in the reactant as

† See Gasser and Richards (loc. cit.).

shown in Fig. 4.4. By using $G^\ominus$ rather than U we allow for changes in the density of the energy states as well as changes in energy along the reaction coordinate. In this theory of reaction rates an important parameter is v_k. Since

$$\frac{k}{v_k} = \exp\left(-\frac{\Delta H_{\ddagger}^{\ominus}}{RT}\right) \exp\left(\frac{\Delta S_{\ddagger}^{\ominus}}{R}\right).$$

different choices of v_k, while not affecting $\Delta H_{\ddagger}^{\ominus}$, will alter $\Delta S_{\ddagger}^{\ominus}$. Hence the value of $\Delta S_{\ddagger}^{\ominus}$ derived from an Arrhenius plot will depend upon the value of v_k that is chosen.

and so on

————

————

and so on

≡≡≡

$q_{\ddagger} > q_R$
$\Delta S_{\ddagger}^{\ominus} +$ ve

Transition
state less
ordered

$q_{\ddagger} < q_R$
$\Delta S_{\ddagger}^{\ominus} -$ ve

Transition
state more
ordered

and so on

————

————

————

Reactant

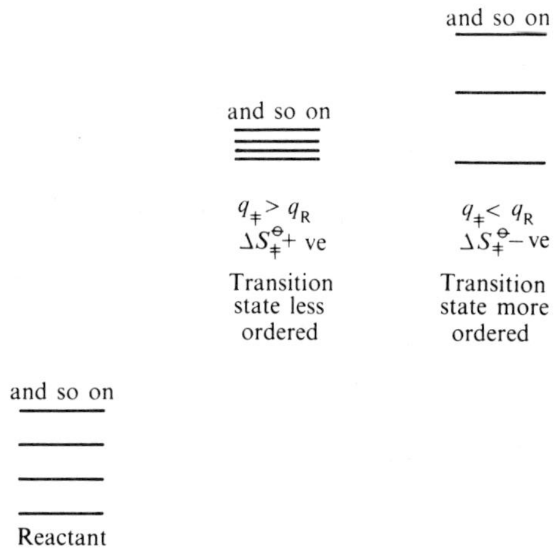

FIG. 4.4. Molecular interpretation of $\Delta S_{\ddagger}$ showing why it is important to consider $\Delta G_{\ddagger}^{\ominus}$ and not just the difference in energy of the lowest states.

Multistep nature of reactions in solution

Now the argument so far has referred to the 'final rate-determining process'. In the gas phase (except at low pressures) this will be a collision which transfers energy. In solution on the other hand the whole process of even the simplest reaction is a multi-molecular process involving several steps. The reaction does not take place in one smooth process over a single energy barrier as shown in Fig. 4.1. Instead we can write in general that the reaction has to proceed through the following stages:

1. Diffusion together of reactants or diffusion of reactant to electrode
2. Arrangement of ionic atmosphere suitable for transition state
3. Orientation of solvent suitable for transition state
4. Atom or electron transfer.

The argument from Fig. 4.3 leading to eqn (4.11) refers to the final rate-determining process, usually the atom or electron transfer; it does not refer to the whole journey from the isolated reactants to the transition states. For one man to climb Everest many many men have to go up and down the foothills between Katmandu and the Khumbu glacier. Similarly in the reaction profile, as shown in Fig. 4.5 the first stages of the reaction are all in equilibrium and can be treated by thermodynamics. Only the last step, the final process, has to be treated as a rate process.

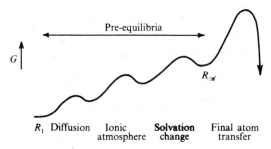

FIG. 4.5. Free-energy profile of reaction in solution emphasizing that such reactions are multimolecular, multi-step processes. The final precursor R_∞ is in equilibrium with the most stable reactant molecules R_1.

Hence we distinguish between R_1 a normal reactant, and R_∞ the precursor of the final process. From eqn (4.6)

$$\text{rate} = k_\Sigma[R_\infty] \tag{4.14}$$

Because R_∞ is in equilibrium with R_1 from (4.13)

$$[R_\infty] = [R_1]\frac{q_{R_\infty}}{q_{R_1}}\exp\left(-\frac{\Delta U_R}{k_B T}\right) \tag{4.15}$$

where ΔU_R is the difference in energy between R_1 and R_∞. Substitution in (4.14) from (4.8) and (4.15) gives

$$k_{obs} = v_k\frac{q_\ddagger}{q_{R_1}}\exp\left(-\frac{\Delta U_\ddagger}{k_B T}\right) \tag{4.16}$$

where $\Delta U_\ddagger$ is the difference in energy between the transition state and the reactant R_1. Note that in the quantitative expression for the observed rate constant the parameters referring to the intermediate R_∞ have vanished. In terms of free energy eqn (4.16) becomes

$$\frac{k_{obs}}{v_k} = \exp\left(-\frac{\Delta G_\ddagger^\ominus}{RT}\right) \tag{4.17}$$

where $\Delta G_{\ddagger}^{\ominus}$ now refers to the difference in free energy between the reactant R_1 and the top of the barrier.

Tafel law as a linear free-energy relation

The Tafel law is the simplest example of a linear free-energy relationship.† When we plot (3.40), (3.42), or (3.43) we are in effect plotting

$$\ln k_E' \quad \text{against} \quad E$$

or, using (4.17)

$$\Delta G_{\ddagger}^{\ominus} \quad \text{against} \quad \Delta G_{TD}^{\ominus}.$$

The linear variation of $\Delta G_{\ddagger}^{\ominus}$ with $\Delta G_{TD}^{\ominus}$ can also be seen in Fig. 1.3. Fig. 4.6 shows some typical results obtained by Klatt and Blaedel for the reaction

$$Co(NH_3)_6^{3+} + e^- \xrightarrow{k_E'} Co(\text{II})$$

These results are plotted according to (3.43):

$$\log(i_C/i_L) = \log k_E' - \log k_D' = \log k_{E=0}' - \log k_D' - \frac{\alpha EF}{2 \cdot 3RT}$$

They show the excellent linear relation between $\log k_E'$ and potential. For comparison purposes Fig. 4.6 also shows a typical Brønsted plot for a simple proton-transfer reaction:

$$RCO_2H + N_2C(CH_3) \cdot COCH_3$$
$$\downarrow k \qquad\qquad\qquad\qquad \text{Rate-determining step}$$
$$RCO_2^- + N_2^+ CH(CH_3) \cdot COCH_3$$
$$\downarrow H_2O \qquad\qquad\qquad \text{fast}$$
$$RCO_2H + N_2^+ + HO \cdot CH(CH_3) \cdot COCH_3$$

In order to compare the thermodynamic scales along the x-axis the Tafel plot is made not only against the practical e.m.f. scale but also against pK_E where

$$pK_E = \log\left(\frac{EF}{2 \cdot 3RT}\right)$$

and is directly comparable to the pK_A scale of dissociation constants. Again notice how only $0 \cdot 2$ V is equivalent to the difference between CH_3CO_2H and $Cl_2CH \cdot CO_2H$ as catalysts. The Tafel plot is obtained from one current–voltage curve. The Brønsted plot was the result of 72 different experiments. The similarity between the plots is apparent. In the electrochemical case we know that we are altering the field at the electrode solution interface.

---

† See Shorter's *Correlation analysis in organic chemistry: an introduction to linear free energy relationships* (OCS 11) for a discussion of other LFER.

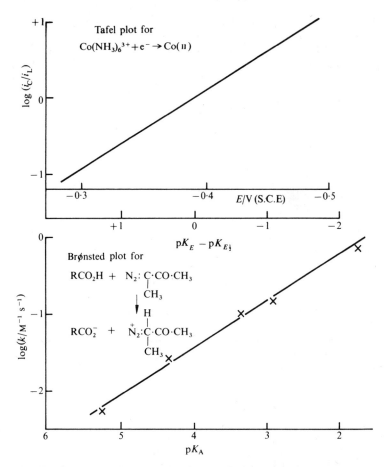

FIG. 4.6. Typical Tafel plot and typical Brønsted plot. Tafel plot has two scales on the x-axis, the practical scale of E measured against a saturated calomel electrode and, to compare with the pK_A scale, pK_E where $pK_E = \log[EF/(2 \cdot 3RT)]$.

In the case of the proton transfer a similar effect is achieved through the inductive effects of the different groups. But now in order to understand the electron transfer in more detail we return to the theories of Marcus and Levich.

Separation of steps

While (4.16) and (4.17) do not contain any parameters connected with R_∞, yet the reaction is broken down into a number of successive steps. How do we know that this must be done? The answer is concerned with the time scales on which the different processes take place. After the reactants have diffused together the following changes will have to take place on moving from reactant to product:

		Time scale
1.	Electron transfer	10^{-16} s.
2.	Alterations to ligand ion bond distances	10^{-14} s.
3.	Re-orientation of solvent dipoles	10^{-11} s.
4.	Re-orientation of ion atmosphere	10^{-8} s.

We have also listed typical times in which these processes take place. Now Fig. 4.7 shows schematically a plot of a reactant changing to a product in which two features A and B have to be altered. We assume that process A takes place much faster than process B. Because of this the reaction cannot take place along the dotted line connecting Q to P since the time taken for the A coordinate to change is far too small for any change on the B coordinate. Hence the reaction has to follow the solid lines. It moves like a rook in chess rather than a bishop. This principle is quite general. We have already used it in discussing the effect of the diffuse double layer on electrode kinetics. Fig. 4.8 shows this particular situation. Or it can be applied to the theory of kinetic salt effects as shown in Fig. 4.9. The Debye–Hückel theory of salt effects works so well because there is a genuine pre-equilibrium of reactants with different ion atmospheres. The reaction selects those particular reactants having an atmosphere which is peculiar for the reactant but particularly suitable for the transition state.

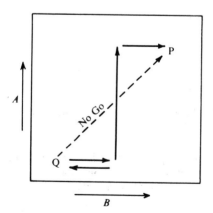

Fig. 4.7. Separation of steps for multistep reaction in solution because of differing time scales. Displacement along the A coordinate is too fast to allow displacement along the B coordinate leading to the 'rook-not-bishop' rule.

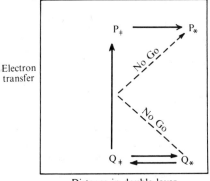

FIG. 4.8. Application of 'rook-not-bishop' rule to diffusion close to the electrode and the actual e^--transfer.

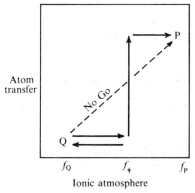

FIG. 4.9. Application of 'rook-not-bishop' rule to kinetic salt effects. Debye–Hückel theory works because there is a genuine pre-equilibrium.

The actual electron-transfer process is the fastest process of all. The adjustment of the charge cloud is much faster (10^{-16} s) than even the movement of the atomic nuclei (10^{-14} s). This is the Franck–Condon principle and is why in Fig. 4.2 the arrows are drawn vertically. During the time of the electronic transition there is no time for the nuclei to alter their positions. Exactly the same principle applies to the final electron transfer in the reactions we are considering. On a time-scale of 10^{-16} s all the nucleii are 'frozen' and appear to be stationary. This situation is drawn in Fig. 4.10. However, the electronic

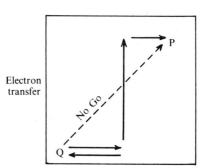

FIG. 4.10. Application of 'rook-not-bishop' rule to final electron-transfer. This is the same as the Franck–Condon principle (see Fig. 4.2). However in an e^--transfer reaction there is no $\pm h\nu$ and so it is isoenergetic.

transition differs from those drawn in Fig. 4.2 since no light is absorbed or emitted. Hence when the electron is transferred there is no change in energy. This is an important central feature of the Marcus and Levich theories. In the final electron transfer there is no change in energy. In terms of quantum mechanics we write the Schrödinger equation:

$$H\Psi = U\Psi$$

where this equation and Ψ refers to the reactant and its surrounding solvent. We can then use the Born–Oppenheimer approximation to separate out the description of the electrons from the rest of the heavy particles:

$$\Psi \simeq \psi_e(x_e)\psi_n(x_n)$$

For the rapid sub-system (the electron) x_n is fixed and we have as a function of x_e:

$$H_e\psi_e = U_e\psi_e. \tag{4.18}$$

For the slower movements of the nucleii:

$$H_n\psi_n = U_\Sigma\psi_n, \tag{4.19}$$

where U_Σ is the total energy and the variable in this equation will be x_n. There will be no mention of x_e in eqn (4.19) but the Hamiltonian H_n contains U_e in the potential energy function, where U_e is a function of x_n when (4.18) has been solved at each value of x_n. The electron transfers first with no change in U_e and secondly with no change in U_Σ. These conditions are satisfied by the interaction of the ion with the solvent dipoles and with its ligands. Due to chance fluctuations around the reactant the necessary conditions are fulfilled and the non-radiative electron transfer can then take place.

Electron transfer (homogeneous)

Fig. 4.11 shows schematically the effect of changing the solvation coordinate on U_e, the energy for the electrons. The change in the solvation of P and Q is represented by the squares, diamonds and circles; the square represents the most stable arrangement of solvent molecules for Q, the diamond for P, and the circle an intermediate arrangement which is appropriate for the transition state. The curve represents the potential-energy function that would be in H_e in eqn (4.18). It changes with x_n as shown. This is for a generalized homogeneous reaction†

$$R_I + O_{II} \rightleftarrows (R_I, O_{II}) \rightarrow (O_I, R_{II}) \rightleftarrows O_I + R_{II}$$
$$Q \qquad\qquad P$$

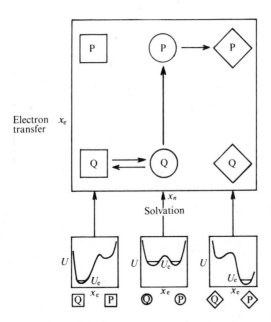

FIG. 4.11. Variation of energy in homogeneous electron transfer. The e^- transfer takes place at the isoenergetic point. The squares, circles and diamonds represent the solvation changes. The insets show the effect of the solvation changes on the potential energy function for the electron, which is contained in H_e in eqn (4.18) leading to the solutions U_e.

† The reaction is assumed to take place by the 'outer sphere' mechanism.

In a particular example

$$Fe^{2+} + Ti^{4+} \rightarrow Fe^{3+} + Ti^{3+},$$

$$R_I \qquad O_{II} \qquad O_I \qquad R_{II}$$

Q would be (Fe^{2+}, Ti^{4+})

P would be (Fe^{3+}, Ti^{3+})

and x_e would measure the distance between Fe and Ti ($=0$ in Fe).

Comparison with fluorescence

Further support for the important role of solvent reorganization can be found from studies of the fluorescence of organic compounds in solution. It is often found that the maximum of the absorption band (corresponding to the $(0,0)$ transition) is at higher frequency than the maximum of the fluorescence band (still the $(0,0)$ transition). The separation between the maxima depends on the solvent. Some typical results are shown in Fig. 4.12.

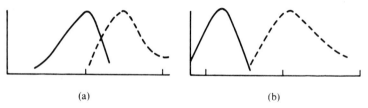

(a)   (b)

FIG. 4.12. Absorption and fluorescence bands for dimethylnaphtheurhodine in (a) hexane and in (b) ethanol. The bands in each case are the $(0,0)$ transition but there is a pronounced separation in the maxima which depends on the solvent.

The corresponding solvent–electron transfer diagram is given in Fig. 4.13. The square represents Q in its proper solvation shell and the diamond represents the solvation shell of Q*. The light is absorbed or emitted so quickly that the 'rook not bishop' rule applies, and, because energy is being supplied by the light, the system cycles round and round the chessboard.

Tunnelling

An important point to notice in Fig. 4.11 is that the energy profile for the electron transfer is W-shaped with a hump separating Q and P. In atom transfers the system would normally have to climb over the barrier separating Q and P; it behaves classically and is treated theoretically with potential energy surfaces (Fig. 4.1) and transition state theory. However Bell's work on proton transfer reactions in solution showed that in certain cases H^+ could

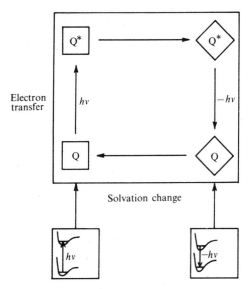

Fig. 4.13. Electron transfers and solvation changes in absorption and fluorescence. Insets show energy changes; the solvation energy change has been exaggerated for clarity.

tunnel through the barrier. Further cases of H^+ tunnelling have been proved by Caldin and his co-workers. This work on H^+ tunnelling is most important since it demonstrates that for H^+ tunnelling is marginal. We are therefore able to conclude that tunnelling for atoms heavier than H^+ will be negligible and the system will behave classically. However, for the electron, which is 1/2000 times the mass of the proton, the transition has to be treated by quantum mechanics. The system will not behave in a classical fashion and need not pass over the top of the barrier. Furthermore the electron will be able to tunnel through much wider barriers than those for H^+. For atom transfer the atom is transferred between reactants which are adjacent to each other and the distance travelled by the atom is ~ 0.1 nm. An electron transfer on the other hand could take place over distances up to ten times as large (~ 1 nm). This may be important when species are strongly repelled from the electrode by a field in the diffuse double layer.

We shall not explore the complexities of the calculation of the transition probability for the system to move along the electron transfer coordinate rather than return back to reactant. Levich has shown that this factor can be separated out and is a constant. It is independent of temperature since electronic energy levels are too widely spaced to be excited at ordinary temperatures. Hence we can take this term and include it in a transmission coefficient κ. If every time the system reaches the critical value of x_n the electron transfers, $\kappa = 1$, the system is then said to be adiabatic. For non-adiabatic transitions the system passes through the critical value of x_n but electron transfers do not take place every time leading to $\kappa < 1$.

Electron transfer (electrode)

A further problem arises in the case of the electrode reaction and that is that the electrode contains a band structure stuffed with electrons in different levels. Fig. 4.14 shows this schematically. The boundary between the filled states and the empty ones is called the Fermi level (U_F). It has been shown that if electrons are taken from the electrode they are taken from the levels close to the Fermi level; the more stable electrons are left alone. Similarly if electrons are transferred to the electrode they are transferred to levels just above the Fermi level. It would be a slower process to ride the parabola in Fig. 4.15 to a higher energy in order to transfer the electron into a higher level.

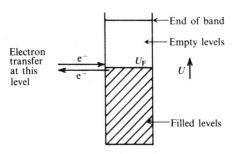

FIG. 4.14. Electron transfers to and from the metal take place close to the Fermi level.

Thus to a good approximation we can consider the reacting electron to be e_F^- and we do not have to concern ourselves with the other levels in the electrode.

Then we draw the equivalent of Fig. 4.11 for the generalized electrode reaction‡

$$Q \;\rightarrow\; P + e_F^-$$

A particular example would be

$$Fe^{2+} \;\rightarrow\; Fe^{3+} + e^-$$

where

Q would be $\quad(Fe^{2+})_* \mathbin{\Big|} Pt$

P would be $\quad(Fe^{3+})_* \mathbin{\Big|} Pt$

‡ We have called the reactant Q and the product P rather than R and O so that they have the same labels as the homogeneous case.

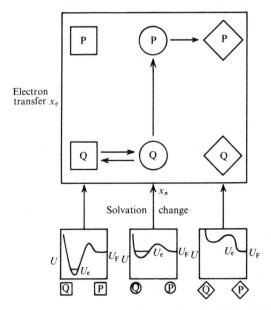

Fig. 4.15. Energy changes in electron transfer to and from an electrode. Insets show change in U that is in H_e in eqn (4.18). In this simplified version the solvation change $P \rightleftarrows P \rightleftarrows P$ has no effect on the Fermi level or U_e. It does have an effect through eqn (4.19) on U_Σ, the total energy.

and

x_e would measure the distance from the electron to the electrode.

A comparison of Figs. 4.11 and 4.15 shows that in the insets in Fig. 4.14 only the energy on the left hand side is altered while in Fig. 4.11 changes in solvation alter the electronic energies on both sides. This is because the Fermi level in the metal is not affected by the solvation changes. In the homogeneous case both of the partners in the electron transfer are sensitive to changes in solvation.

Solvent re-organization

A detailed theory of this process has been worked out by Levich and Dogonadse. They assume that in a polar solvent the main change that takes place along the solvent coordinate is the chance fluctuations of the solvent dipoles around the ions. It is shown that the variation of potential energy U_n with displacement along the solvent coordinates is parabolic, as shown in Fig. 4.16. This is equivalent to assuming that the solvent undergoes simple harmonic oscillations. This will probably be true for small perturbations.

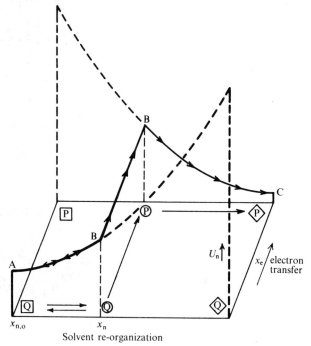

FIG. 4.16. Changes in solvation energy for an electron transfer reaction. The electron transfer can only take place at the iso-energetic point.

For this model in (4.19) the potential energy function U_n in H_n has the form

$$U_n = U_0 + \tfrac{1}{2}hv_s\Sigma(x_n - x_{n,0})^2$$

where

x_n is a solvent coordinate

$x_{n,0}$ is its equilibrium value

and

U_0 is the potential energy when all $x_n = x_{n,0}$.

The U_e of eqn (4.18) has apparently vanished from this equation. The reason for this is that U_0 contains the value of U_e when all $x_n = x_{n,0}$ and the second term contains the effect of the solvent fluctuations on U_e. It has a Σ to contain all the different coordinates. To plot U_n as a function of these different coordinates we would need many dimensions. Even the Russians have only three so we simplify the pictorial representation by plotting the fluctuations of the solvent along one solvent coordinate. Hence the change in potential energy for the solvent part of the reaction can be plotted as in Fig. 4.16. The three-dimensional picture can be further simplified by plotting it in two dimensions as in Fig. 4.17.

Now we can bring in the third dimension again and imagine that we have two solvent coordinates x_1 and x_2. The equivalent of the simplified form of Fig. 4.17 will then be two intersecting paraboloids as shown in Fig. 4.18.

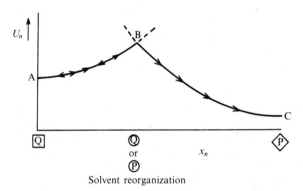

Solvent reorganization

FIG. 4.17. Simplified version of Fig. 4.16 showing the barrier to the reaction is concerned with solvent changes.

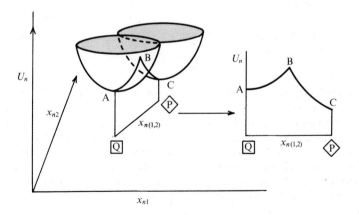

FIG. 4.18. The intersection of two parabolic bowls still produces the same shape as Fig. 4.17. The electron-transfer takes place at B where the bowls intersect at the lowest energy.

The least energetic course for the reaction will still go up one parabola and down another giving the same picture as we obtained with one coordinate, when plotted along $x_{1,2}$. We see that the main process requiring activation is not the electron's climbing to the top of the barrier in Fig. 4.11 or 4.15 but the movement of the system along the solvent coordinate from A to B in Fig. 4.17. From coordinate geometry given in Appendix (7) we find the activation energy (A to B) in terms of the energy difference between A and C to be:

$$U_{\ddagger} = \frac{(U_A + U_S)^2}{4U_S}, \tag{4.20}$$

where

$U_{\ddagger}$ is the activation energy for this step

U_A is the change in energy between Q and P

and

U_S describes the change in solvation energy to alter the solvation of Q to that of P (or vice versa) without any electron transfer.

Levich and Dogonadse derive these results as a special case of their full quantum mechanical treatment. Marcus takes a less specific model of the solvent and has a more statistical mechanical approach. He ends up with a similar expression to eqn (4.20) except that it is in terms of free energy,

$$G_{\ddagger} = \frac{(G_A + G_S)^2}{4G_S}. \tag{4.21}$$

Fig. 4.19 shows the significance of the quantities in these equations. In the Levich–Dogonadse model if one takes in (4.11) $v_k = v_S \sim 10^{11}\,s^{-1}$ where v_S is the frequency of solvent molecules re-orienting one finds that $\Delta S_{\ddagger} = 0$. We then have the special case

$$G_{\ddagger} = U_{\ddagger}$$

and for this particular model eqns (4.20) and (4.21) are identical. Even though the Levich model (taken with $v_k = v_S$) gives $\Delta S_{\ddagger,0} = 0$—that is the spacing between levels remains constant in the activation process—it is more general, as discussed above, to use free energy rather than energy and so we shall use eqn (4.21) rather than (4.20). The more general theory of Marcus also takes into account changes in the bond lengths attaching the ligands to the central ion. The Levich–Dogonadse model is almost certainly over simplified but the importance of their more specific treatment is that

1. It is a quantum mechanical calculation of the rate of a chemical reaction.
2. It suggests the use of v_S rather than $k_B T/h$ as the correct v_k for certain reactions in solution.

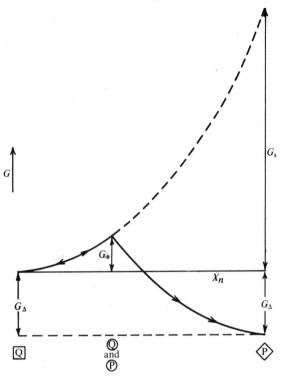

Fig. 4.19. Significance of quantities in (4.21). The free energy of activation $G_\ddagger$ is a function of the equilibrium quantity, G_Δ, and the free energy necessary to re-organize the solvent from G_S.

3. It provides a model of the role of the solvent for which calculations can be made.
4. It emphasises that an important part of the activation process is the alterations in the solvation coordinate(s).
5. Being a general solution it specifies the conditions when the simpler version presented here will be found.

Expression for rate constant for homogeneous reactions

Now in order to see if this model agrees with experiment we have to combine all the various parts of the calculation into an expression for the observed rate constant. We will deal with the homogeneous case first:

$$k_2 = K_Q \nu_S \kappa \exp\left(-\frac{G_\ddagger}{RT}\right) \tag{4.22}$$

where

k_2 is the second-order rate constant

K_Q describes the diffusion pre-equilibrium which brings the reactants together to form Q as in (4.1)

v_S is the right value of v_k to use in this case

κ contains the transition probability

and

$G_{\ddagger}$ is given by (4.21).

Now we can express G_Δ the difference between Q and P in terms of the overall change of free energy $\Delta G_{TD}^{\ominus}$ by writing

$$\Delta G_{TD}^{\ominus} = \Delta G_{Q}^{\ominus} + G_\Delta - \Delta G_{P}^{\ominus}$$

or

$$G_\Delta = \Delta G_{TD}^{\ominus} - \Delta G_{Q}^{\ominus} + \Delta G_{P}^{\ominus} \qquad (4.23)$$

where

$\Delta G_{Q}^{\ominus}$ is for the pre-equilibrium such as

$$Fe^{2+} + Ti^{4+} \quad \rightleftarrows \quad (Fe^{2+}, Ti^{4+})$$
$$Q$$

and

$\Delta G_{P}^{\ominus}$ for the same type of equilibrium for the products

$$Fe^{3+} + Ti^{3+} \quad \rightleftarrows \quad (Fe^{3+}, Ti^{3+})$$
$$P$$

This is shown in Fig. 4.20.

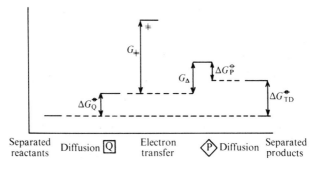

FIG. 4.20. Significance of free-energy quantities in (4.23). The figure drawn for an uphill reaction so that all terms are +ve. For a downhill reaction G_Δ and $\Delta G_{TD}^{\ominus}$ will be negative.

The observed free energy of activation would be given by

$$\Delta G_{\ddagger}^{\ominus} = \Delta G_{Q}^{\ominus} + G_{\ddagger}.$$

Rate constant for electrode reaction

By a very similar argument we obtain for the rate constant for the electrode reaction

$$k' = K'_{E}\nu_{S}\kappa \exp\left(-\frac{G_{\ddagger}}{RT}\right) \qquad (4.24)$$

where

$$G_{\ddagger} = \frac{(G_{A}+G_{S})^2}{4G_{S}}$$

and

$$G_{A} = \Delta G_{TD}^{\ominus} - \Delta G_{Q}'^{\ominus} + \Delta G_{P}'^{\ominus} \qquad (4.25)$$

where $\Delta G_{Q}'^{\ominus}$ is for pre-equilibria such as

$$(Q)_{\infty} \rightleftarrows (Q)_{*} \left\| Pt \right.$$

and $\Delta G_{P}'^{\ominus}$ is similar for the products

$$(P)_{\infty} \rightleftarrows (P)_{*} \left\| Pt. \right.$$

Tafel relation

The Tafel relation can be derived from eqns (4.24) and (4.25) since ΔG_{TD} depends on the potential. We have for α the slope of the Tafel plot which is defined in eqn (1.20) and measured from (3.40) or (3.42),

$$\alpha = \frac{RT}{F}\frac{\partial \ln k'}{\partial E} = -\frac{\partial G_{\ddagger}}{F\partial E}$$

$$= -\left(\frac{1}{2F}\right)\left(1+\frac{G_{A}}{G_{S}}\right)\frac{\partial G_{A}}{\partial E}$$

$$= \left(\frac{1}{2}\right)\left(1+\frac{G_{A}}{G_{S}}\right). \qquad (4.26)$$

Hence we find that when G_{S} is large compared to G_{A} implying that the kinetics are slow but the thermodynamics are roughly in balance, $\alpha \approx \frac{1}{2}$. This is found to be the case in many reactions. Indeed Fig. 1.3 was drawn for $\alpha = \frac{1}{2}$. On the other hand for fast reactions, where G_{S} is small, the theory predicts that α will not be constant. Close to $E = E^{\ominus}$, where $G_{A} \approx 0$, $\alpha \approx \frac{1}{2}$. But if the reaction is very uphill as shown in Fig. 4.21 $G_{A} \approx G_{S}$ and $\alpha \rightarrow 1$.

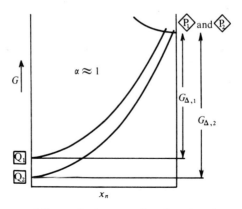

FIG. 4.21. Extreme uphill case. $G_{\ddagger}$ almost equal to G_Δ and so changes in G_Δ are also seen in $G_{\ddagger}$ and $\alpha \approx 1$.

On the other hand when it is very downhill as shown in Fig. 4.22, $G_\Delta \approx -G_S$ and $\alpha \to 0$. Hence for fast reactions we might expect that α decreases continuously as the reaction is driven harder. This has indeed been found by Frumkin for the $Fe(CN_6)^{3-}/Fe(CN_6)^{4-}$ system and by Parsons for the Cr^{3+}/Cr^{2+} system. Some of Frumkin's experimental results are shown in Fig. 4.23. It is easy to see the change in slope from $\alpha > \frac{1}{2}$ on the left-hand side (see Fig. 4.21) to $\alpha < \frac{1}{2}$ on the right-hand side (see Fig. 4.22). Parsons and Passeron found for the Cr^{3+}/Cr^{2+} system that

$$\alpha = 0{\cdot}40 + 0{\cdot}26 E_\eta.$$

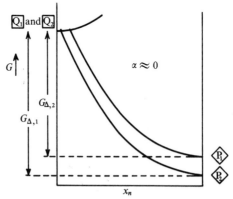

FIG. 4.22. Extreme downhill case. Changes in G_Δ make very little difference to small $G_{\ddagger}$ and so $\alpha \approx 0$.

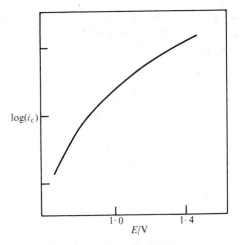

FIG. 4.23. Curved Tafel plot for $Fe(CN)_6^{3-}/Fe(CN)_6^{4-}$ as system changes between extremes shown in Fig. 4.21 and 4.22. Data from A. N. Frumkin, D. A. Petry, and N. N. Nickolaeva-Fedorovich, *Electrochim. Acta*, 1963, **8**, 177.

Since G_Δ varies with the overpotential E_η this is in reasonable agreement with the theoretical equation (4.26).

Comparison of homogeneous and heterogeneous rates

Marcus was able to use the theory to compare the rates of homogeneous and heterogeneous electron transfer. We take the particularly simple symmetrical system where $\Delta G_{TD}^\ominus = 0$ and $G_\Delta = 0$. We write it out with symbols to represent the solvation changes:

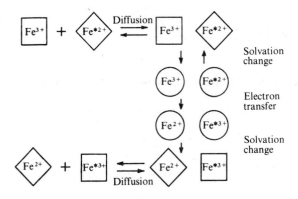

At the electrode the system is symmetrical when $E = E^{\ominus}$ as discussed in Fig. 3.15. At this potential the rates for oxidation and reduction are equal (k_0') so $G_A = 0$ and $\alpha = \frac{1}{2}$. Hence we can write:

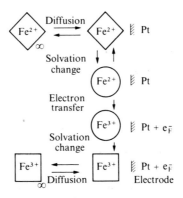

Now in the solvation changes the homogeneous system has two Fe species changing while at the electrode only one species changes. Hence if $G_{S,Fe}$ is the free-energy change for

$$\boxed{Fe^{3+}} \longrightarrow \left(Fe^{3+}\right)$$

or

$$\left\langle Fe^{2+}\right\rangle \longrightarrow \left(Fe^{2+}\right)$$

then for the homogeneous reaction

$$G_S = 2G_{S,Fe}$$

and for the electrode reaction

$$G_S = G_{S,Fe}$$

Substitution in (4.22) and (4.24), together with $G_A = 0$, gives

$$k_2 = K_Q \nu_S \kappa \exp\left(-\frac{G_{S,Fe}}{2RT}\right) \tag{4.27}$$

and

$$k_0' = K_E' \nu_S \kappa \exp\left(-\frac{G_{S,Fe}}{4RT}\right). \tag{4.28}$$

We now need values for K_Q, ν_S, and K'_E. As discussed above

$$\nu_S \approx 10^{11} \, s^{-1}. \tag{4.29}$$

The pre-equilibrium constant K_Q for getting the two reactants close together will have values in the range:

$$1 \, mol^{-1} \, dm^3 > K_Q > 0 \cdot 1 \, mol^{-1} \, dm^3 \tag{4.30}$$

The pre-equilibrium constant K'_E describes the localizing of the reactant on a plane close to the electrode. A typical value is

$$K'_E = 1 \, nm.$$

The products $K'_E \nu_S$ can be regarded as the collision number Z' in (1.6) and

$$Z' = K'_E \nu_S \sim 10^2 \, m \, s^{-1} \ . \tag{4.31}$$

Ignoring κ, we can now compare (4.27) and (4.28) since

$$\exp\left(-\frac{G_{S,X}}{4RT}\right) \approx \frac{k'_0}{K'_E \nu_S} = \frac{k'_0}{10^2} \tag{4.32}$$

$$\approx \sqrt{\left(\frac{k_2}{K_Q \nu_S}\right)} = \sqrt{\left(\frac{k_2}{10^{11}}\right)}, \tag{4.33}$$

where

k'_0 is expressed in $m \, s^{-1}$,
k_2 is expressed in $dm^3 \, mol^{-1} \, s^{-1}$,

and

$G_{S,X}$ is the solvent re-organization free energy for the X/X^- system.

Now we test the model against experimental data. Table 4.1 shows the comparison made by Marcus of these values. Considering the approximations made in the derivation, the agreement between results from two very different types of experiment is striking, and provides support for the solvation model. Furthermore those systems which are highly organized and where there is little solvent reorganization to be done have low values of $G_{S,X}$ and fast reactions, for instance MnO_4^-/MnO_4^{2-} and $Fe(CN)_6^{3-}/Fe(CN)_6^{4-}$. On the other hand, those systems which are more loosely solvated and where the solvation changes will be larger will have higher values of $G_{S,X}$ and hence slower reactions. The reason for this is indicated in Fig. 4.24.

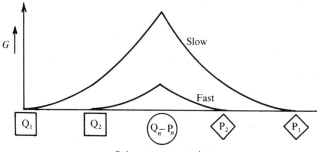

FIG. 4.24. Schematic indication of reason why reactions requiring small amount of solvent reorganization, e.g. $Fe(CN_6)^{3-}/Fe(CN)_6^{4-}$, are faster than those requiring a lot of reorganization, e.g. Eu^{3+}/Eu^{2+}. The reactions considered are the symmetrical ones, hence $G_\Delta = 0$ and for the homogeneous case P_n is identical to Q_n.

TABLE 4.1

Comparison of the rates of symmetrical homogeneous and electrochemical electron transfer reactions

Homogeneous $O + R \underset{k_0'}{\overset{k_2}{\rightleftarrows}} R + O$

Heterogeneous $O + e^- \rightleftarrows R$ at $E = E^\ominus$

O	$\sqrt{(k_2/10^{11})}$	$k_0'/10^2$
$Fe(CN)_6^{3-}$	10^{-3}	10^{-5}
MnO_4^-	2×10^{-4}	2×10^{-5}
Fe^{3+}	9×10^{-6}	7×10^{-7}
V^{3+}	4×10^{-7}	4×10^{-7}
Eu^{3+}	6×10^{-8}	3×10^{-8}
$Co(NH_3)_6^{3+}$	$<5 \times 10^{-11}$	5×10^{-12}

Taken from R. A. Marcus, *J. phys. Chem.*, 1963, **67**, 853.

Homogeneous cross reactions

With values of $G_{S,X}$ for each single-electron couple Marcus has shown that one can describe the rates of homogeneous cross reactions with eqn (4.21). That is, knowing G_I and G_{II} where

$$G_S = 2G_I \quad \text{for the isotopic exchange}$$

$$O_I + R_I^* \rightleftarrows R_I + O_I^*$$

and

$$G_S = 2G_{II} \quad \text{for the isotopic exchange}$$

$$O_{II} + R_{II}^* \rightleftarrows R_{II} + O_{II}^*,$$

we can write that for the cross reaction

$$O_I + R_{II} \xrightarrow{k_{I,II}} R_I + O_{II},$$

$$G_S = G_I + G_{II},$$

and hence with (4.21)

$$\Delta G_{\ddagger} = \frac{(G_\Delta + G_I + G_{II})^2}{4(G_I + G_{II})}$$

$$= \tfrac{1}{4}(G_I + G_{II}) + \tfrac{1}{2}G_\Delta + \frac{G_\Delta^2}{4(G_I + G_{II})}.$$

Assuming that $K_Q = K_P$ and ignoring κ we then obtain

$$\ln k_{I,II} = \tfrac{1}{2}(\ln k_{I,I} + \ln k_{II,II}) + \tfrac{1}{2}\ln K_{I,II}$$

$$+ \frac{(\ln k_{I,II})^2}{8[\ln(k_{I,I}/K_Q v_S) + \ln(k_{II,II}/K_Q v_S)]} \tag{4.34}$$

where $K_{I,II}$ is the equilibrium constant for the reaction.

Table 4.2 shows that (4.34) does indeed work reasonably well. In electrochemical thermodynamics the electrode potentials of half cells have proved most valuable for calculating the position of equilibria. From n separate values of $E^\ominus$ one can calculate $\tfrac{1}{2}n(n-1)$ equilibrium constants. In kinetics G_I, G_{II} etc. play a similar role to that of $E^\ominus$. Again n measurements allow the estimation (rather than calculation since it is only kinetics) of $\tfrac{1}{2}n(n-1)$ homogeneous rate constants. Hence we are now starting to discover the underlying pattern which governs the rates of electron transfer reactions.

TABLE 4.2

Comparison of observed and calculated values for homogeneous electron transfers

Reaction		Observed	Calculated
O_I	R_{II}	$k_{I,II}/dm^3\ mol^{-1} \cdot s^{-1}$	$k_{I,II}/dm^3\ mol^{-1}\ s^{-1}$
Ce (IV)	$W(CN)_8^{4-}$	$> 10^8$	$6 \cdot 1 \times 10^8$
Ce (IV)	$Fe(CN)_6^{4-}$	$1 \cdot 9 \times 10^6$	$6 \cdot 0 \times 10^6$
Ce(IV)	$Mo(CN)_8^{4-}$	$1 \cdot 4 \times 10^7$	$1 \cdot 3 \times 10^7$
$IrCl_6^{2-}$	$W(CN)_8^{4-}$	$6 \cdot 1 \times 10^7$	$8 \cdot 1 \times 10^7$
$IrCl_6^{2-}$	$Fe(CN)_6^{4-}$	$3 \cdot 8 \times 10^5$	$5 \cdot 7 \times 10^5$
$IrCl_6^{2-}$	$Mo(CN)_8^{4-}$	$1 \cdot 9 \times 10^6$	$1 \cdot 0 \times 10^6$
$Mo(CN)_8^{3-}$	$W(CN)_8^{4-}$	$5 \cdot 0 \times 10^6$	$1 \cdot 7 \times 10^7$
$Mo(CN)_8^{3-}$	$Fe(CN)_6^{4-}$	$3 \cdot 0 \times 10^4$	$2 \cdot 7 \times 10^4$
$Fe(CN)_6^{3-}$	$W(CN)_8^{4-}$	$4 \cdot 3 \times 10^4$	$5 \cdot 1 \times 10^4$

Taken from R. J. Campion, N. Purdie, and N. Sutin, *Inorg. Chem.* 1964, **3**, 1091.

Calculation of electrode rate constants

So far the tests of the model and the theory have been by correlations of experimental data or in the case of the Tafel relationship by observing the rate as a function of the potential. A more stringent test would be to try and calculate $G_{S,X}$ from molecular parameters. The calculation of a rate constant for a reaction in solution is a formidable task because of the complicated multi-molecular nature of the reaction. However, Hale has attempted to calculate the parameter $G_{S,X}$ from an electrostatic model of the solvent together with force constants for the metal–ligand bonds. His results are compared with experiment in Table 4.3. They are reported as values of

$$\Delta G_{\ddagger,S}^{\ominus} = \tfrac{1}{4}G_S \quad \text{when } G_A = 0.$$

Some of his results for the reduction of aromatic hydrocarbons are also given. The agreement is reasonable except for Ce(IV) and Co(III).

TABLE 4.3

Comparison of experimental and calculated free energies of activation for $O + e^- \rightleftarrows R$

O	Experimental $\Delta G_{\ddagger}^{\ominus}/kJ\,mol^{-1}$	Calculated $\Delta G_{\ddagger}^{\ominus}/kJ\,mol^{-1}$
$Fe(CN)_6^{3-}$	29	30
WO_4^{2-}	34	36
MnO_4^-	34	37
$Fe(H_2O)_6^{3+}$	36	38
$V(H_2O)_6^{3+}$	37	37
$Mn(H_2O)_6^{3+}$	41	45
$Ce(H_2O)_6^{4+}$	50	28
$Cr(H_2O)_6^{3+}$	52	42
$Co(H_2O)_6^{3+}$	56	38
Naphthalene (in DMF)	23	24
Tetracene (in DMF)	22	21

DMF = N,N-dimethylformamide.
Taken from J. M. Hale, *Reactions of molecules at electrodes*, (ed. N. S. Hush), Wiley, 1971, p. 229.

Conclusions

Simple electron-transfer reactions take place by changes in the solvation and metal–ligand distances such that the radiationless iso-energetic electron-transfer can take place. This process can be described theoretically and expressions for rate constants can be obtained from molecular parameters and without recourse to transition-state theory. Agreement is found between experiment and theory in the following features:

1. For most electrode reactions $\alpha \approx \frac{1}{2}$.
2. For fast electrode reactions the Tafel plot is curved as in Fig. 4.22.
3. There is a good correlation between symmetrical homogeneous electron transfers and the electrode reaction at $E = E^{\ominus}$.
4. The rates of homogeneous cross reactions can be correlated with parameters from (3).
5. G_S can be estimated from the molecular parameters and is in reasonable agreement with experiment.

The extension of the successful theoretical description of electron-transfer reactions to other reactions in solution, for instance proton transfer, is already being carried out by Marcus and by Dogonadse. So we end this chapter by a comparison of the two simplest reactions in solution electron and proton transfers:

Comparison of electron and proton transfers

	Electron transfer	Proton transfer
Thermodynamics measured as	$E^{\ominus}$ for $O + \frac{1}{2}H_2 \rightleftarrows R + H_{aq}^+$	K_A for $HA \rightleftarrows H_{aq}^+ + A$
Kinetics measured as	i leading to i_0 or k_0'	c versus t leading to k
LFER (see Fig. 4.6)	Tafel plot $\log i$ versus E	Brønsted plot $\log k$ versus pK_A
Gradient of LFER (see Figs. 4.21 and 4.22)	α or β Measures symmetry of transition state	α or β Measures symmetry of transition state
Shift to diffusion control (see Fig. 3.12 and 3.14)	i/E plot shows limiting current when electrode is very active	Brønsted plot flattens out at diffusion controlled limit for downhill reactions to O and N bases.
Curvature of LFER (see Fig. 4.23)	'Fast' reactions give curved Tafel plots	Some reactions also give curved Brønsted plots.
Bond breaking	No bonds made or broken	At least one covalent bond is made and one broken.
Time for actual transfer	10^{-16} s Franck–Condon principle	10^{-14} s May involve other nuclear motions.
Tunnelling	Yes	Found in many reactions but not all.
Solvation	Main barrier to reaction is altering solvation and ligand distances	Solvent reorganization is only one of the terms contributing to the free energy barrier.

	Electron transfer	*Proton transfer*
Alone in the solution	e_{aq}^- is now well characterized but is unstable in H_2O (lifetime $\sim 10~\mu s$)	H_3O^+ well characterized and stable. Enjoys (?) particular relation with H_2O leading to anomalous mobility.
Isotope effects	Wish there were lots of heavy electrons which would stay put!	D and T very useful for investigating details of H^+ transfer.

Because the electron tunnels we can see the important role of the solvent in the kinetics of electron-transfer reactions. From the similarities between the Tafel and Brønsted behaviour one hazards a guess that the role of the solvent may be just as crucial for H^+ transfers and for other reactions in solution.

5. Multistep processes

Introduction

In this chapter we consider several different examples of more complicated electrode mechanisms and we also describe two techniques, the ring-disc electrode and cyclic voltammetry which are useful for investigating intermediates in multistep processes. The examples are chosen to illustrate how electrochemical techniques can be used to measure the rates of fast homogeneous reactions, how electrochemical systems obey the Hammett plot, the range and diversity of electro-organic chemistry and the importance of adsorption.

Hitherto we have discussed reactions involving a single electron transfer. This is because this is the simplest basic reaction at an electrode. Reactions which involve more than one electron will in general proceed by successive single electron steps, The reason for this can be seen from the discussion in Chapter 4. Imagine the general system:

$$A + e^- \rightarrow B \qquad (5.1)$$

$$B + e^- \rightarrow C \qquad (5.2)$$

where for instance A might be Tl(III), B Tl(II), and C Tl(I). The system can be thought to change from A to C either in two steps as shown in eqns (5.1) and (5.2) or in one step involving two electrons:

$$A + 2e^- \rightarrow C \qquad (5.3)$$

It is likely that the solvation of, and arrangement of ligands around, B will be intermediate between A and C. Thus B provides a 'half-way house' and this means that as shown in Fig. 5.1 by going through B there will be two smaller free-energy barriers rather than one large one. It is easier to take two bites at the cherry rather than swallowing it in one gulp. Thus more complicated electrode mechanisms are analysed into a succession of steps; these steps are either single electron transfers or 'chemical steps', The term 'chemical step' describes a reaction which does not involve the transfer of charge to or from the electrode. We start by considering a system in which a chemical step precedes the electron transfer. This type of mechanism is called CE (Chemical Electron).

Preceding chemical reaction (CE)

An example of this type of process is the reduction of H^+ from a buffer solution containing a weak acid. We may describe the system:

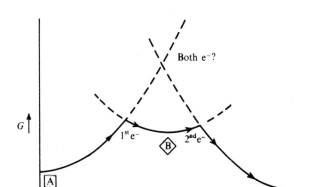

Solvent reorganization

FIG. 5.1. Schematic diagram to show why in general in the over-all change A $\xrightarrow{2e^-}$ C the electrons go in one at a time (A $\xrightarrow{e^-}$ B $\xrightarrow{e^-}$ C) rather than two at a time (as per Noah's ark).

$$\text{Solution} \quad HA \underset{k_{-1}}{\overset{k_1}{\rightleftharpoons}} H^+ + A^- \quad K_A \qquad (5.4)$$

$$c_{HA} \qquad\qquad c_H \quad c_A$$

$$\text{Electrode} \quad H^+ + e^- \longrightarrow \tfrac{1}{2}H_2.$$

HA does not react.

These systems have been studied on a rotating platinum disc electrode by Vielstich and Jahn and by Albery and Bell. At the electrode H^+ can be reduced but not HA; in the solution the concentration of HA (c_{HA}) is much greater than that of H^+ (c_H) since HA is a weak acid. Experimental conditions are chosen so that

$$c_A > 10\, c_{HA}$$

and therefore c_A can be treated as a constant throughout the solution, and this is true even at the electrode. We will now calculate the limiting current for the particular case where the electrode is so reducing that all the H^+ reaching the electrode is immediately reduced. We ignore the complications introduced by the double layer. The equilibrium (5.4) will be in balance in the bulk of the solution but close to the electrode because H^+ is being removed at the electrode there will be more HA dissociating than H^+ and A^- recombining. As we shall see the distance over which the equilibrium is perturbed in this way is much smaller than the diffusion layer. It will be characterized by a parameter x_R, the thickness of the *reaction layer*. Thus as shown in

Fig. 5.2 the problem can be separated into two parts, firstly the description of the concentrations very close to the electrode in the reaction layer and secondly the description of the transport from the bulk of solution to the outside of the reaction layer.

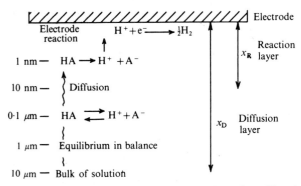

Fig. 5.2. Example of a system with a preceding chemical reaction taking place in the reaction layer.

Because c_{HA} greatly exceeds c_H it is HA which supplies the protons for the electrode reaction and the flux is related to its transport through the diffusion layer. From (3.10) we obtain

$$j_{L,R} = \frac{D(c_{HA,\infty} - c_{HA,R})}{x_D} \tag{5.5}$$

where $c_{HA,R}$ is the concentration of HA just outside the reaction layer, and $j_{L,R}$ has the subscripts to remind us that the electrode is removing all the H^+ and therefore it is a limiting flux, with respect to the electrode potential.

In the reaction layer we have for HA:

$$\frac{\partial c_{HA}}{\partial t} = D_{HA}\frac{\partial^2 c_{HA}}{\partial x^2} - k_1 c_{HA} + k_{-1} c_A c_H.$$

This equation is a combination of Fick's second law (see Fig. 3.6) and an ordinary equation for homogeneous kinetics describing the removal and production of HA. Since we have a steady state at the electrode,

$$\frac{\partial c_{HA}}{\partial t} = 0$$

and so

$$D_{HA}\frac{\partial^2 c_{HA}}{\partial x^2} = k_1 c_{HA} - k_{-1} c_A c_H. \tag{5.6}$$

This equation describes a steady state concentration profile, where diffusion balances the formation and decomposition of HA. Similarly for H^+

$$D_H \frac{\partial^2 c_H}{\partial x^2} = +k_1 c_{HA} - k_{-1} c_A c_H. \tag{5.7}$$

The boundary conditions for these equations are: first at the electrode, where $x = 0$,

$$c_H = 0 \text{ since } H^+ \text{ is destroyed on the electrode,} \tag{5.8}$$

$$\frac{\partial c_{HA}}{\partial x} = 0 \text{ since HA does not react at the electrode,} \tag{5.9}$$

and secondly for $x > x_R$ just outside the reaction layer,

$$c_{HA} = c_{HA,R}{}^\dagger \text{ by definition} \tag{5.10}$$

and

$$c_H = \frac{k_1 c_{HA,R}}{k_{-1} c_A}, \text{ equilibrium in balance.} \tag{5.11}$$

We now define a function c' which describes the breakdown of the equilibrium between HA and H^+:

$$c' = \frac{K_A}{c_A} \cdot c_{HA} - c_H. \tag{5.12}$$

When the equilibrium is in balance $c' = 0$ but near the electrode where $c_H = 0$

$$c'_O = \frac{K_A c_{HA,O}}{c_A}. \tag{5.13}$$

In Appendix 8 we derive the following relation for c',

$$c' = c'_O \exp(-x/x_R), \tag{5.14}$$

where

$$x_R = \sqrt{\left(\frac{D_H}{k_{-1} c_A}\right)}. \tag{5.15}$$

The distance x_R is the distance over which a proton once formed has a chance to diffuse before it meets an A^- and is turned back into HA. The lifetime, τ_H of the proton is $(k_{-1} c_A)^{-1}$ and in a time interval τ_H the proton will diffuse for a distance $\sqrt{(D\tau_H)}$, which is equal to x_R.

† Because $(\partial c_{HA}/\partial z)_0 = 0$ and x_R is small, $c_{HA,O}$ and $c_{HA,R}$ are approximately equal.

Because of the exponential term in eqn (5.14) when $x > x_R$, c' goes rapidly to zero, and the equilibrium comes into balance. A typical value of x_R can be estimated from

$$D_H \simeq 10^{-4} \, \text{cm}^2 \, \text{s}^{-1} = 10 \, \text{m}^2 \, \text{Gs}^{-1}$$

$$k_{-1} = 10^{11} \, \text{M}^{-1} \, \text{s}^{-1} = 0 \cdot 1 \, \text{m}^3 \, \text{mol}^{-1} \, \text{ns}^{-1}$$

$$c_A = 0 \cdot 1 \, \text{M} = 100 \, \text{mol} \, \text{m}^{-3}$$

giving

$$x_R \sim 1 \, \text{nm} \ll x_D \sim 1 \, \mu\text{m}.$$

Fig. 5.3 shows a plot of c' against distance and this is compared with a similar plot of c' for the temperature jump relaxation method for studying fast homogeneous reactions in solution.† In the electrochemical situation the equilibrium is perturbed in a steady state and the perturbation falls off with distance. In temperature jump the variables are reversed; the perturbation is homogeneous but decays with time. The parameter x_R and τ the relaxation time for the temperature jump method play similar roles, and we can compare

$$x_R \simeq \sqrt{\left(\frac{D_H}{k_{-1}c_A}\right)}$$

with

$$\tau \simeq \frac{1}{k_{-1}c_A} \quad \text{for } k_{-1}c_A \gg k_1.$$

Hence the electrochemical method of measuring fast reactions is a relaxation method where the equilibrium is perturbed with respect to distance rather than time.

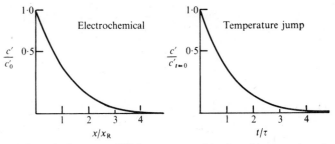

FIG. 5.3. Perturbations to equilibria to measure kinetics of fast reactions. In the electrochemical case the equilibrium as perturbed with respect to distance rather than time.

† See Bradley's *Fast reactions* (OCS 23) for a description of this method.

We return to (5.12) and (5.14) to work out the flux of H^+ at the electrode surface

$$j = D_H \left(\frac{\partial c_H}{\partial x} \right)_{x=0} = -D_H \left(\frac{\partial c'}{\partial x} \right)_{x=0} = \frac{D_H K_A c_{HA,0}}{c_A x_R}. \qquad (5.16)$$

Substitution for x_R gives

$$j = k'_R c_{HA,0},$$

where

$$k'_R = \sqrt{\left(\frac{D_H k_1 K_A}{c_A} \right)}; \qquad (5.17)$$

k'_R has the dimensions of a heterogeneous rate constant (m s^{-1}) and describes how the flux is related through the diffusion and the kinetics in the reaction layer to the concentration of HA just outside the reaction layer. Using (5.5) and (5.17) we can now follow the argument used in Chapter 3 from (3.9) to (3.12) where instead of k' we have k'_R and so

$$\frac{1}{j_{L,R}} = \frac{1}{k'_D c_{HA,\infty}} + \frac{1}{k'_R c_{HA,\infty}}. \qquad (5.18)$$

| Current controlled by transport | Current controlled by homogeneous kinetics |

Plots of the concentration profiles for A^-, HA, and H^+ are shown in Fig. 5.4.

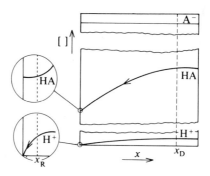

FIG. 5.4. Concentration profiles for reduction of H^+ for weak acid buffer. The discontinuities on the y-axis show differences in at least an order of magnitude between the concentrations of the various species.

Measurement of homogeneous rate constants

The electrochemical technique for measuring the rates of fast homogeneous reactions depends on (5.18). Some typical results for the dissociation of $CMe_3 \cdot CO_2H$ are shown in Fig. 5.5. The results are plotted according to a rearranged form of (5.18).

$$\frac{j_{L,D}}{j_{L,R}} = 1 + \frac{k'_D}{k'_R} = 1 + (\text{constant}) \times W^{\frac{1}{2}}$$

where

$$W \text{ is the rotation speed}$$

and

$$j_{L,D} = k'_D c_{HA,\infty}.$$

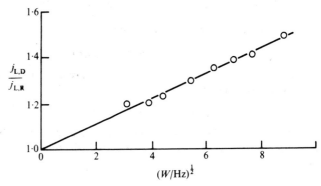

FIG. 5.5. Results for determining the rate constants for $C(Me)_3CO_2H \rightleftarrows C(Me)_3CO_2^- + H^+$. Data from Albery and Bell.

A value of k'_R can be found from the gradient and this gives, using (5.17), a value for k_1, and, from the equilibrium constant, k_{-1}. Results for $CH_3 \cdot CO_2H$ and $CMe_3 \cdot CO_2H$ by this method are given in Table 5.1. The results for acetic acid are in good agreement with those found by Eigen and Eyring and it is satisfactory that the two very different techniques give the same answers within the experimental error.

Thus the electrochemical method can be used to measure the rates of diffusion controlled reactions taking place in the solution.† Another important

† If k_{-1} is diffusion controlled the thickness of the reaction layer is often comparable to that of the diffuse double layer. Rather complicated corrections then have to be carried out to allow for the variations in concentration (e.g. c_A) and for the effect of the field on the transport of H^+ to the electrode.

TABLE 5.1

Values of rate constants for weak acid buffers

	$\dfrac{k_1}{\mu s^{-1}}$	k_{-1} mol m$^{-3}\mu s^{-1}$ or M^{-1}ns^{-1}	
Electrochemical			
CH$_3$CO$_2$H	0·72	41	Albery and Bell
CMe$_3$CO$_2$H	0·115	12·4	
Relaxation technique using second Wien effect			
CH$_3$CO$_2$H	0·90	51	Eigen and Eyring

class of reactions investigated by electrochemical methods are reactions involving metal ions and their ligands. A typical example is:

$$\text{Solution} \qquad \text{Cd(CN)}_4^{2-} \underset{k_{-1}}{\overset{k_1}{\rightleftharpoons}} \text{Cd(CN)}_3^{-} + \text{CN}^{-}$$

$$\text{Electrode} \qquad \text{Cd(CN)}_3^{-} \xrightarrow{2e} \text{Cd} + 3\text{CN}^{-}$$

$$\text{Cd(CN)}_4^{2-} \text{ does not react}$$

The analysis is just the same as that described above and the following rate constants were obtained:

$$k_1 = 20 \text{ ms}^{-1} \qquad k_{-1} = 70 \text{ m}^3 \text{ mol}^{-1} \text{ ms}^{-1} \text{ (or M}^{-1}\,\mu s^{-1}).$$

For the study of electrode kinetics it is important to understand the effect of a preceding chemical reaction. The complete analysis shows that instead of eqn (5.18) we have

$$\frac{1}{j_R} = \frac{1}{k'_D c_{HA,\infty}} + \frac{1}{k'_R c_{HA,\infty}} + \frac{c_A}{K_A k' c_{HA,\infty}}. \qquad (5.19)$$

Transport   Homogeneous   Heterogeneous
                 kinetics   kinetics

This equation shows that for sufficiently large values of k'_R the homogeneous kinetic term is unimportant and the system behaves as a pre-equilibrium followed by a rate-determining electron transfer.

Two-electron reactions (EE)

We now examine the behaviour of systems, such as that given in eqns (5.1) and (5.2), where the reactant can change its oxidation state by two. Nearly all electro-organic systems are in this class and also many inorganic systems. The principles that emerge from our study can also be applied to systems where more than two electrons are involved but they are outside the scope of this book.

The general system can be written:

$$
\begin{array}{ll}
\text{Diffusion in solution} & \text{A}_\infty \qquad\qquad \text{B}_\infty \\
& \quad\downarrow \qquad\qquad\quad \uparrow \\
\text{Electrode} & \text{A}_0 + e^- \underset{k'_{-1}}{\overset{k'_1}{\rightleftarrows}} \text{B}_0 \\
\\
\text{Electrode} & \text{B}_0 + e^- \underset{k'_{-2}}{\overset{k'_2}{\rightleftarrows}} \text{C}_0 \\
\text{Diffusion in solution} & \qquad\qquad\qquad \downarrow \\
& \qquad\qquad\qquad \text{C}_\infty
\end{array}
$$

Examples of such a system are:

A	B	C
Tl(III)	Tl(II)	Tl(I)
Cu(II)	Cu(I)	Cu(0).

We shall assume firstly that the bulk concentration of A is a_∞ and of B and C is zero, and secondly that the diffusion coefficients of A, B, and C are all equal. This last assumption means that we can use the same transport rate constant k'_D for all three species where, as in (3.17),

$$k'_D = D/x_D.$$

At steady state we can write for the different fluxes:

$$
\begin{array}{lll}
j = k'_D(a_\infty - a_0) & \text{Transport of A to electrode} & (5.20) \\
\ = k'_1 a_0 - k'_{-1} b_0 & \text{First electron transfer} & (5.21) \\
\ = k'_D b_0 + k'_2 b_0 - k'_{-2} c_0 & \text{Transport of B away from electrode} & \\
& \quad + \text{second electron transfer} & (5.22) \\
\ = k'_D b_0 + k'_D c_0 & \text{Transport of B and C away from} & \\
& \text{electrode.} & (5.23)
\end{array}
$$

We therefore have four equations and four unknowns (j, a_0, b_0, and c_0). The current is given by:

$$i = AF(k'_D b_0 + 2k'_D c_0),\qquad\qquad (5.24)$$

since each B that is formed requires one electron and each C two electrons. Elimination of the unknowns in (5.20) to (5.24) gives:

$$i = \frac{AF k'_1 k'_D a_\infty}{k'_D + k'_1 + \dfrac{k'_{-1}}{1 + \{k'_2/(k'_D + k'_{-2})\}}}\left(1 + \frac{k'_2}{k'_D + k'_2 + k'_{-2}}\right) \qquad (5.25)$$

This equation looks rather complicated but we will examine various limiting forms of it.

The equation can be expressed more elegantly if we define the following functions:

$$\lambda_1 = \frac{k'_1}{k'_D}, \qquad \lambda_{-1} = \frac{k'_{-1}}{k'_D}, \qquad \lambda_2 = \frac{k'_2}{k'_D + k'_{-2}}.$$

We then obtain

$$\frac{i}{i_L} = \frac{\lambda_1}{1 + \lambda_1 + \lambda_{-1}/(1 + \lambda_2)} \left[1 + \frac{\lambda_2}{1 + \lambda_2} \right] \qquad (5.26)$$

where

$$i_L = AFk'_D a_\infty$$

and is the limiting current for a *one*-electron transfer.

Now we first examine the two different cases at the potential where $\lambda_1 = 1 + \lambda_{-1}$:

	Case I	Case II
	$\lambda_2 \ll 1$ or	$\lambda_2 \gg 1$ or
	$k'_2 \ll k'_D + k'_{-2}$	$k'_2 \gg k'_D + k'_{-2}$
	$\dfrac{i}{i_L} = \dfrac{\lambda_1}{1 + \lambda_1 + \lambda_{-1}}$	$\dfrac{i}{i_L} = \dfrac{2\lambda_1}{1 + \lambda_1 + \lambda_{-1}/\lambda_2}$

$$(5.27)$$

Case I corresponds to the situation where k'_2 is small compared to either k'_D or k'_{-2}. Under these conditions B does not react by the second electron transfer. This is either because the second step is thermodynamically unfavourable ($k'_{-2} \gg k_2$) *or* because the rate constant for the second step is too slow and B diffuses away from the electrode before it has a chance to react ($k'_D \gg k'_2$). The equation for i/i_L is exactly the same as (3.25) (with $j_R = 0$) giving a one-electron wave for the reaction

$$A + e^- \rightarrow B.$$

The half-wave potential is when $\lambda_1 = 1 + \lambda_{-1}$. As the reaction is driven harder λ_1 becomes greater than $1 + \lambda_{-1}$ and

$$\frac{i}{i_L} \rightarrow 1.$$

Then using (5.26), for $\lambda_1 \gg (1 + \lambda_{-1})$,

$$\frac{i}{i_L} \simeq 1 + \frac{\lambda_2}{1 + \lambda_2}.$$

Eventually λ_2 becomes comparable to 1 and the second-electron transfer can take place. A second one-electron wave is then observed with a half-wave potential when $\lambda_2 = 1$, corresponding to the reaction

$$B + e^- \longrightarrow C.$$

When

$$\lambda_2 \gg 1,$$

$$\frac{i}{i_L} \to 2,$$

and now the overall reaction

$$A + 2e^- \longrightarrow C$$

is taking place. Fig. 5.6 shows Case I where we have assumed that both steps are irreversible. Since the electrons go in one at a time we can treat each one-electron wave separately and analyse it by the theory presented in Chapter 3. Thus we need spend no more time or space on Case I.

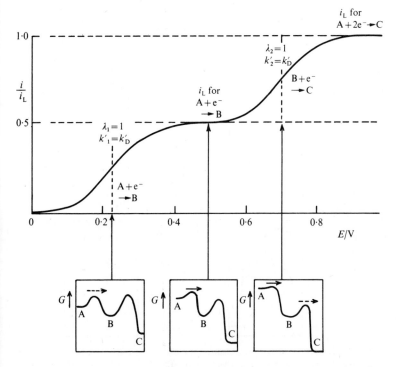

FIG. 5.6. Case I for two irreversible waves ($\lambda_{-1} \ll 1$ or $k'_{-1} \ll k'_D$). Insets show schematic free-energy profiles with the free energy of B plotted at the same height. Note that barriers for $A \to B$ and for $B \to C$ are equal at their respective half wave potentials.

Now in Case II we have when $\lambda_1 = 1 + \lambda_{-1}$

$$k'_2 \gg k'_D + k'_{-2}.$$

This means that the second electron transfer is thermodynamically favourable
($k'_2 \gg k'_{-2}$) *and* that the electrochemical rate constant is sufficiently large
for B to have no chance of diffusing away from the electrode ($k'_2 \gg k'_D$). This
means that the only product of the electrochemical reaction is C and the
overall reaction at the electrode is

$$A + 2e^- \ \rightarrow \ C.$$

Therefore instead of two one-electron waves, we observe only one wave
the height of which corresponds to $2e^-$ per molecule of A. Examples are
shown in Fig. 5.7.

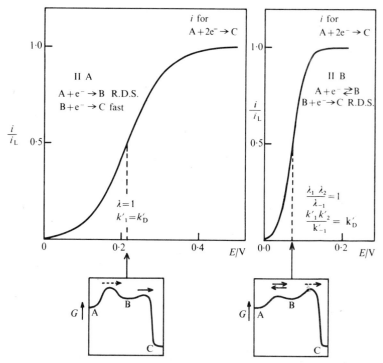

FIG. 5.7. Cases IIA and IIB for two electron waves. In IIA the first step is rate determining and in IIB the second step. Insets show free-energy profiles at the half-wave
potentials; note that the free-energy difference between A and the transition state is
the same in both cases. IIB has a steeper wave than IIA because there is a greater
difference between species A and the transition state and hence the free-energy
difference and the rate constant for case IIB is more sensitive to changes in potential.

From (5.27)

$$\frac{i}{i_L} = \frac{2\lambda_1}{1 + \lambda_1 + \lambda_{-1}/\lambda_2}.$$

We now subdivide this into two further cases:

Case II A	Case II B
$\lambda_{-1}/\lambda_2 \ll 1$	$\lambda_{-1}/\lambda_2 \gg 1$
$k'_{-1} \ll \dfrac{k'_2}{1 + k'_{-2}/k'_D} < k'_2$	$k'_{-1} \gg k'_2$ (assuming $k'_D \gg k'_{-2}$)
$\dfrac{i}{i_L} = \dfrac{2\lambda_1}{1 + \lambda_1}$	$\dfrac{i}{i_L} = \dfrac{2(\lambda_1\lambda_2/\lambda_{-1})}{1 + (\lambda_1\lambda_2/\lambda_{-1})}$

In Case II A the second step is fast compared to the back reaction of B to A. This means that every B formed immediately takes on a second electron,

$$A + e^- \rightarrow B \quad \text{Rate determining}$$

$$B + e^- \rightarrow C. \quad \text{Fast}$$

The result is a two-electron wave with a half-wave potential at $\lambda_1 = 1$. The shape of the wave is the same as the irreversible wave discussed in Chapter 3 but its amplitude is multiplied by two because of the second reaction. It can be analysed in the same way and will give information about the rate constants for the first electron transfer.

In Case II B we first assume that k'_{-2} can be neglected. This is very likely to be the case, since the reaction is being driven from A to C. (Furthermore, if k'_{-2} is important then the whole A–C system is reversible and as discussed in Chapter 3 we cannot obtain any kinetic information.) With the assumption we now have

$$k'_{-1} \gg k'_2 \gg k'_D \gg k'_{-2}.$$

B is now more likely to return to A than to react to C; but it is more likely to do either of these reactions than to diffuse off the electrode. We therefore have a pre-equilibrium followed by the second electron-transfer being the rate determining step:

$$A + e^- \rightleftarrows B \quad \text{pre-equilibrium}$$

$$B + e^- \rightarrow C \quad \text{rate determining.}$$

A two electron wave is observed with a half-wave potential at $\lambda_1\lambda_2/\lambda_{-1} = 1$ or $k'_1k'_2/k'_{-1} = k'_D$.

This is shown in Fig. 5.7. At first sight the waves for Case II A and Case II B appear very similar; each is a single two electron wave. However the II B wave will rise more steeply than the II A wave because the transfer coefficient for II B will be $\sim 1\frac{1}{2}$ rather than $\frac{1}{2}$. This arises from the fact that the II B transition state contains one more electron than that belonging to II A

The difference between Cases II A and II B lies in the relative size of k'_{-1} and k'_2. These two rate constants alter in different directions with the potential. Hence which step is rate determining depends on the potential of the electrode. Assuming $\alpha = \frac{1}{2}$ for each step, Fig. 5.8 shows a plot of the variation of the rate constants with potential and the critical value where the rate determining step alters when $k'_2 = k'_{-1}$. At this potential the free energies of the first and second transition states are equal. The rate constant for the back reaction,

$$C \;\longrightarrow\; A + 2e^-,$$

is also plotted. Since the reaction is passing over the same free energy surface at any potential the transition state is the same for the forward and backward reactions:

	$\vec{k}'$	$\overleftarrow{k}'$
	Forward	Backward
Rate constant for $k'_2 > k'_{-1}$	k'_1	$\dfrac{k'_{-2}k'_{-1}}{k'_2}$
Rate constant for $k'_{-1} > k'_2$	$\dfrac{k'_1 k'_2}{k'_{-1}}$	$k'_{-2}.$

There is no reason why the change in the rate determining step (the potential where $k'_{-1} = k'_2$) should be the same as $E^\ominus$ the potential where $k'_1 k'_2 = k'_{-1}k'_{-2}$ and for an equimolar mixture of A and C the system is in thermodynamic equilibrium. The relative position of these two potentials can give a number of different cases. In Fig. 5.8 we have drawn a common situation where the two potentials are not widely separated and the system is irreversible. The current–voltage curve for an equimolar mixture of A and C is shown and it consists of two separated waves. It is most important to note that the two waves have *different* rate-determining steps. For

$$A + 2e^- \;\longrightarrow\; C$$

the rate determining step is

$$A + e^- \;\longrightarrow\; B$$

followed by a fast step

$$B + e^- \;\longrightarrow\; C.$$

For

$$C \;\longrightarrow\; A + 2e^-$$

the rate-determining step is

$$C \;\rightarrow\; B + e^-$$

followed by a fast step

$$B \;\rightarrow\; A + e^-.$$

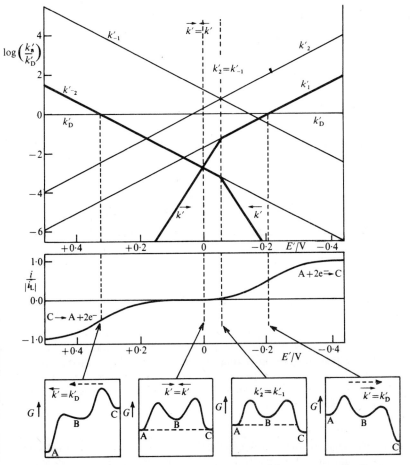

FIG. 5.8. Plot of rate constants, current–voltage curve, and free-energy profiles for an irreversible A, C system with equal concentrations of A and C. The effective rate constants for the electrochemical reactions are $\vec{k}'$ and $\bar{k}'$. Strictly they go through a curve rather than an obtuse angle at $k_2' = k_{-1}'$. The variable describing the voltage is E' where $E' = E - E_{12}^{\ominus}$ and $E_{12}^{\ominus}$ is the standard electrode potential for the A, C system.

This is a general pattern which is in accord with the Hammond postulate. The harder a reaction is driven the earlier will be the transition state. For

$$A + 2e^- \rightarrow C,$$

$$\vec{k}'_{obs} = \frac{k'_1 k'_2}{k'_{-1} + k'_2},$$

$$-E\uparrow, \qquad k'_2\uparrow, \qquad k'_{-1}\downarrow, \qquad \text{and} \qquad \vec{k}'_{obs} \rightarrow k'_1.$$

And for

$$C \rightarrow A + 2e^-,$$

$$\overleftarrow{k}'_{obs} = \frac{k'_{-2} k'_{-1}}{k'_2 + k'_{-1}},$$

$$E\uparrow, \qquad k'_{-1}\uparrow, \qquad k'_2\downarrow, \qquad \text{and} \qquad \overleftarrow{k}'_{obs} \rightarrow k'_{-2}.$$

In each case the first electron-transfer is rate determining.

It may appear that one is claiming that the forward and backward reactions can have different transition states—a claim which has led to excommunication from the Society for Electrochemistry with the solemn elders intoning 'what about the principle of microscopic reversibility?'. The point is that at any potential in Fig. 5.8 the principle is obeyed. But we can only observe the forward and backward reactions at different potentials. The potential alters the rate constants and hence the rate-determining step. Thus forward and backward reactions measured at different potentials do not necessarily have the same transition state. Furthermore the same reaction measured at different potentials may not follow the same mechanism. This is an important conclusion and warns us that it is dangerous to assume that a mechanism established in one range of potential holds at all potentials.

For multi-electron processes we cannot in general follow the procedure shown in Fig. 3.29 to find $E_{\frac{1}{2}}^{\ominus}$. Thus as shown in Fig. 5.9 extrapolation of the rate constants does not give $E_{\frac{1}{2}}^{\ominus}$, but the potential where $k'_1 = k'_{-2}$—a number that may be interesting to kineticists but is not thermodynamic information. The extrapolation procedure can be only used if the sum of $\alpha + \beta$ for each process adds up to the number of electrons, since in that case, there has been no shift in rate-determining step.

Copper system

The reduction of Cu^{2+} exemplifies the difference between two one-electron waves and one two-electron wave. In the presence of Cl^- the $Cu(I)$ state is stabilized and so in Fig. 5.10 we see two one-electron waves corresponding to Case I,

$$Cu^{2+} + e^- \rightarrow Cu^+ \qquad \text{First wave}$$

$$Cu^+ + e^- \rightarrow Cu \qquad \text{Second wave}$$

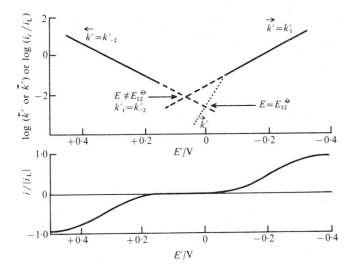

FIG. 5.9. Part of Fig. 5.8 showing that extrapolated Tafel plots do *not* intersect at $E = E_{12}^{\ominus}$ when there has been a change in the rate determining step.

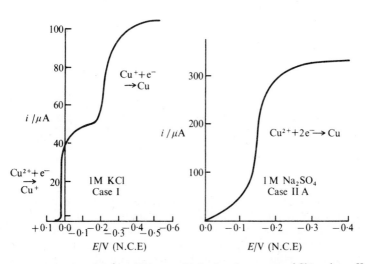

FIG. 5.10. Reduction of Cu^{2+} exhibits case I behaviour in presence of Cl^- and case II behaviour with no Cl^- present. With Cl^- the intermediate $Cu(I)$ state (B) is mainly $CuCl_2^-$ and is therefore more stable. Data from L. N. Nekrasov and N. P. Berezina.

However with no Cl^- present Cu^+ is unstable and we find only one two-electron wave corresponding to Case II A

$$Cu^{2+} + e^- \rightarrow Cu^+ \quad \text{Rate-determining step}$$

$$Cu^+ + e^- \rightarrow Cu \quad \text{Fast.}$$

Electron and proton transfers in organic electrochemistry

An important class of reactions in organic electrochemistry consists of the addition to an unsaturated system of two electrons and two protons. The reaction may be written in general:

$$A + 2H^+ + 2e^- \rightleftarrows CH_2$$

where A contains a double bond or a conjugated set of double bonds. Examples of A and CH_2 are given in Table 5.2.

TABLE 5.2

Typical organic systems of the A/CH_2 *type*

A	CH_2
$-C\equiv C-$	$-CH=CH-$
$>C=C<$	$>CH-CH<$
$>C=O$	$>CH-OH$
$-N=O$	$-NH-OH$
1,4-benzoquinone (O=⟨ring⟩=O)	hydroquinone (HO-⟨ring⟩-OH)

The reason why the overall electrochemical reaction involves two electrons and two protons is firstly because organic species in general have closed shells. Odd-electron species (radicals) are in general less stable and therefore the one-electron transfer not followed by a second electron transfer is uncommon. Secondly the protons are involved because in general for lone pairs in C, N, or O

$$X: + H^+ \rightarrow XH$$

is downhill. This is not true in all cases for O; for instance in basic solutions

and even

are stable.

However in general we can analyse the mechanism of these reactions by the 'scheme of squares' in which electron transfers are written across the page and proton transfers down the page:

There are six possible routes for going from A to CH_2 by successive electron and proton transfers. The route followed will depend both on the pH and on the electrode potential. In a well-buffered solution the proton transfers are likely to be rapid compared to the electron transfers. Hence we can normally assume that each vertical line in the scheme of squares is in equilibrium, and at any concentration of H^+ the system reduces to the two-electron case considered in the previous section:

$$\Sigma A \underset{k'_{-1}}{\overset{k'_1}{\rightleftarrows}} \Sigma B \underset{k'_{-2}}{\overset{k'_2}{\rightleftarrows}} \Sigma C.$$

However these rate constants will now depend on pH. In the simple case one of the six different transition states E_1 to E_6 will have the highest free energy and passage through that highest state will control the rate of reaction. For the six different states Table 5.3 lists the order of the observed rate constant with respect to $[H^+]$ and also how sensitive the rate constant is to potential.

The shift in transition state with pH in a vertical line is at the dissociation constant of the transition state. For example the shift from E_1 to E_3 will take place where the pH equals the pK for the following 'equilibrium':

$$(ABH)_{\ddagger} \rightleftarrows (AB)_{\ddagger} + H^+.$$

$$E_3 \qquad\qquad E_1$$

TABLE 5.3

Dependence of electrochemical rate constants on pH and potential for the different transition states E_1 to E_6

		A $\quad$ E_1	B$^{\cdot-}$ $\quad$ E_2	C^{2-}			
		AH$^+$ $\quad$ E_3	BH$^\cdot$ $\quad$ E_4	CH$^-$			
		AH$_2^{2+}$ $\quad$ E_5	BH$_2^{\cdot+}$ $\quad$ E_6	CH$_2$			
		A $\rightarrow$ CH$_2$				CH$_2$ $\rightarrow$ A	
	α				β		
k_1'	$\frac{1}{2}$	E_1	0	$\dfrac{k_{-2}'k_{-1}'}{k_2'}$	$\frac{3}{2}$	E_1	-2
	$\frac{1}{2}$	E_3	1		$\frac{3}{2}$	E_3	-1
	$\frac{1}{2}$	E_5	2		$\frac{3}{2}$	E_5	0
$\dfrac{k_1'k_2'}{k_{-1}'}$	$\frac{3}{2}$	E_2	0	k_{-2}'	$\frac{1}{2}$	E_2	-2
	$\frac{3}{2}$	E_4	1		$\frac{1}{2}$	E_4	-1
	$\frac{3}{2}$	E_6	2		$\frac{1}{2}$	E_6	0

For more acid solutions the reaction will go through E_3 and for more basic solutions the reaction will go through E_1.

Quinone/hydroquinone system

An example of this type of system is the quinone/hydroquinone system studied by Vetter. Fig. 5.11 shows the crude experimental data as plots of $\log |i|$ against potential. The straight lines are parts of the current–voltage-curve corresponding to a Tafel slope for a single electron transfer.·

For the reaction

$$+ \; 2H^+ + 2e^- \longrightarrow$$

A $\qquad\qquad$ CH$_2$

at a pH < 4 the order with respect to H$^+$ is $+1$ and hence the transition state is E3.

For a pH > 4.5 the order with respect to H$^+$ for those parts of the curves corresponding to the single electron transfer is 0 and hence the transition state is E_1. The pK of $(ABH)_+^{\cdot}$ is ~ 4.3. At more alkaline pHs less of the curves

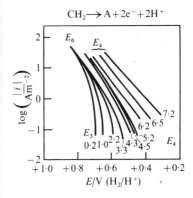
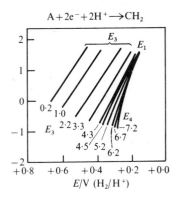

FIG. 5.11. Tafel plots for quinone/hydroquinone system on Hg at different pHs. Each plot is labelled with its pH. E_n refers to the transition state of the rate determining step. Curvature is caused by shift in rate determining step from 1st to 2nd electron transfer. Data from K. J. Vetter, *Z. Elektrochem.*, 1952, **56**, 797.

correspond to the single electron transfer and the second transition state (E_2, E_4, or E_6) plays a larger part; this is shown by the steeper Tafel slopes. The same effect can be seen in Figs. 5.8 and 5.9 where the change in gradient is the obtuse angle in log $\vec{k}'$ at $k_2' = k_{-1}'$. A similar type of behaviour is found for the reverse reaction

$$\text{(hydroquinone)} \longrightarrow \text{(quinone) A} + 2H^+ + 2e^-$$

At a pH > 5.2 the order with respect to H^+ is -1 and this corresponds to E_4 as the transition state. At pH < 5 the order with respect to H^+ for the single electron-transfer parts of the curve is zero, corresponding to transition state E_6. At more acid pHs the second transition state (E_1, E_3, or E_5) interferes more giving steeper Tafel plots. We can therefore summarize in Table 5.4 the different transition states as a function of pH. The routes are listed using the notation introduced before. The chemical step denoted by C in this case is a proton transfer. The change over between E_1 and E_4 at pH ~ 7 and between E_6 and E_3 at pH ~ 2 is caused by a shift in the ratio of k_2'/k_{-1}' with pH. For E_1 and E_4,

$$H^+ + (AB)_\ddagger \xrightarrow{k'_{-1}} \ ? \xrightarrow{k'_2} (BCH)_\ddagger$$

$$E_1 \qquad\qquad\qquad E_4$$

$$\frac{k'_2}{k'_{-1}} \propto [H^+]$$

and therefore at alkaline pHs k'_{-1} tends to become larger than k'_2 leading to a pre-equilibrium followed by the rate determining step for $A \rightarrow CH_2$. For E_3 and E_6,

$$(BCH_2)_\dagger \xrightarrow{k'_2} \ ? \xrightarrow{k'_{-1}} (ABH)_\dagger + H^+,$$

$$E_6 \qquad\qquad\qquad E_3$$

$$\frac{k'_{-1}}{k'_2} \propto \frac{1}{[H^+]}$$

and therefore in acid solutions k'_2 becomes greater than k'_{-1} and for the reverse reaction $CH_2 \rightarrow A$ this means that there is a pre-equilibrium followed by a rate determining step; that is for the back reaction, passage through the second transition state E_3 determines the rate of the reaction.

TABLE 5.4

Quinone/hydroquinone system

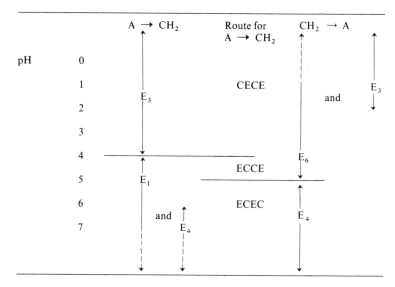

The ring–disc electrode

If the intermediates formed in a multistep electrode process are not too short-lived they can be detected and their rates of reaction measured by using a ring–disc electrode. This type of electrode was first developed by Frumkin and Nekrasov in Moscow. It consists of a disc electrode surrounded by a concentric ring electrode as shown in Fig. 5.12. The insulating gap between the electrodes is typically only 50 μm. Because of the pattern of flow established at a rotating disc, species which leave the disc electrode are swept outwards. The ring electrode is downstream of the disc and so a fraction of the species leaving the disc will reach the ring. The ring electrode is set to a potential which destroys the species when they arrive. Fig. 5.13 shows the arrangement schematically. The transport by convection and diffusion of species from the disc to the ring can be solved exactly; the fraction of the species that leave the disc electrode which react on the ring electrode rather than being lost in the bulk of solution is given by N. Theory and experiment show that N is simply a function of the geometry of the electrode.

Consider a multistep process:

$$\text{Disc electrode A} \xrightarrow[n_1]{k'_1} \text{B} \xrightarrow[n_2]{k'_2} \text{C}$$

$$\downarrow k_D \text{ Diffusion}$$

Solution and ring electrode

where n_1 and n_2 electrons are involved in each step.

Now B can diffuse into the solution or react further to form C. The ring electrode is set to a potential so that the reaction

$$\text{Ring electrode} \quad \text{A} \xleftarrow[n_1]{\text{fast}} \text{B}$$

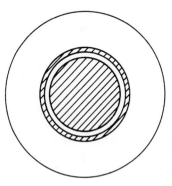

FIG. 5.12. End-on view of a ring–disc electrode. Typical dimensions are: radius of disc, 4·0 mm, inner radius of ring, 4·1 mm, outer radius of ring, 4·3 mm.

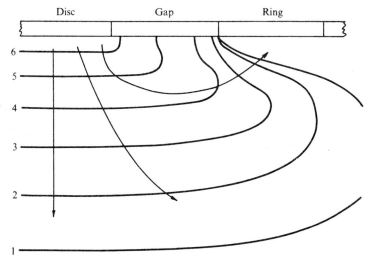

FIG. 5.13. Schematic concentration gradient for an intermediate or product escaping from the disc either to the bulk of the solution or to destruction on the ring–electrode.

takes place at a fast enough rate to convert all the B reaching the ring electrode back to A. In the steady state we may write for the fluxes:

$$\text{disc} \quad j_1 = j_2 + j_D \quad \text{and} \quad j_D/j_2 = k'_D/k'_2$$

$$\text{ring} \quad j_R = N j_D.$$

Then

$$\frac{|i_R|}{|i_D|} = \frac{n_1 j_R}{n_1 j_1 + n_2 j_2}$$

$$= \frac{N n_1 j_D}{(n_1 + n_2) j_2 + n_1 j_D}$$

$$= \frac{N}{1 + (1 + n_2/n_1) k'_2/k'_D}. \tag{5.26}$$

This is the *Ivanov–Levich equation*. When k'_2 is small compared to k'_D the right-hand side gives N; all of B leaves the disc electrode and none of it reacts in the second step. But when k'_2 is large compared to k'_D then a much smaller fraction leaves the disc electrode.

If

$$k'_2 > 10^3 k'_D$$

then such a small fraction reaches the ring that it becomes difficult to detect.

Note that $k_2'/k_D' = \lambda_2$ (when $k_{-2}' = 0$) and that the two cases discussed here parallel the earlier discussion of Cases I and II.

Copper system

One of the first systems to be studied in 1962 by Nekrasov and Berezina using a ring–disc electrode was the reduction of Cu^{2+}. In the scheme given above we have:

$$\text{Disc electrode} \quad Cu^{2+} \xrightarrow{k_1'} Cu^+ \xrightarrow{k_2'} Cu$$

$$k_D' \quad \text{Diffusion}$$

$$\text{Ring electrode} \quad Cu^{2+} \xleftarrow{\text{fast}} Cu^+.$$

In the presence of Cl^- the Cu^+ is stabilized and the reaction on the disc gives two separate one-electron waves as shown in Fig. 5.14 which has the same disc polarogram as Fig. 5.10.

The first wave is the reduction of Cu^{2+} to Cu^+. The Cu^+ formed can be oxidized on the ring and in the region of the first plateau the ratio of the currents is N. After the first plateau the Cu^+ to Cu reaction starts on the disc and so we get the second wave. As this process becomes faster less and less Cu^+ escapes into the solution and so the ring current falls to zero.

In the presence of SO_4^{2-}, rather than Cl^-, the Cu^+ is less stable. Only one wave is seen in the disc. However the Cu^+ intermediate can still be detected and measured on the ring as shown in Fig. 5.15. Note that the ring current is very much smaller than in Fig. 5.14. Thus the reduction of Cu^{2+} does indeed take place one electron at a time through the unstable Cu^+ intermediate.

Nitrobenzene system

The reduction of nitrobenzene in alkaline solution has been studied by Nekrasov, Gerischer, and Kastening amongst others. It takes place through the radical anion. The system can be written:

$$\text{Disc electrode} \quad \phi NO_2 \rightarrow \phi NO_2^{\cdot-} \rightarrow \phi NO \rightarrow \phi NHOH$$

$$\text{Ring electrode} \quad \phi NO_2 \leftarrow \phi NO_2^{\cdot-} \qquad \phi NO \leftarrow \phi NHOH$$

$$\text{I} \qquad\qquad\qquad\qquad \text{II}$$

Fig. 5.16 shows some typical results on a gold ring–disc electrode. As the nitrobenzene is reduced on the disc electrode, to start with the main product is the radical anion which escapes to the ring where it is converted back to nitrobenzene in the region of ~ -0.5 to -0.6 V (wave I). For more oxidizing potentials on the ring any phenylhydroxylamine produced is also oxidized

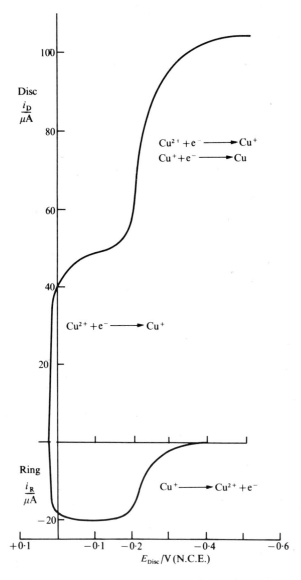

FIG. 5.14. Reduction of Cu^{2+} in presence of Cl^- at a ring–disc electrode. The $Cu(I)$ product of the first wave causes the ring current. Data from L. N. Nekrasov and N. P. Berezina.

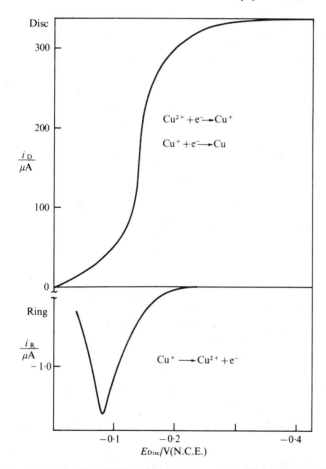

FIG. 5.15. Reduction of Cu^{2+} in the absence of Cl^- at a ring–disc electrode. A small amount of the Cu(I) intermediate escapes into the solution and causes a much smaller ring current than in Fig. 5.14.

but in this case only as far as nitrosobenzene. This is the reason for wave II in the potential range -0.1 to -0.4 V. As the potential on the disc becomes more reducing the radical anion wave I increases to a maximum at (4) and then decreases to zero when the radical-anion instead of escaping to the ring is further reduced on the disc to phenylhydroxylamine. The current due to the phenylhydroxylamine increases throughout. Fig. 5.17 shows the ring current due to the radical anion in 3 mol dm^{-3}-NaOH as a function of the disc current and it can be seen that the maximum in the ring current occurs at about

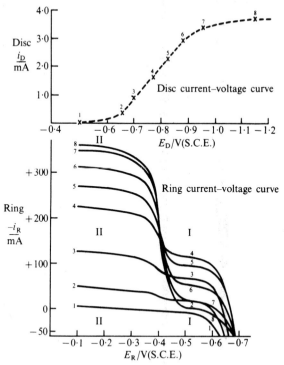

FIG. 5.16. Results on a ring–disc electrode for the reduction of nitrobenzene. The lower figure shows the polarograms for oxidizing the species reaching the ring at different points on the disc current–voltage curve. Wave I is caused by the intermediate ϕNO_2^- and wave II by the product $\phi NHOH$. Data from the author's own laboratory measured by E. M. Wormald.

one-quarter of the limiting disc current. This is because one electron is needed to reduce nitrobenzene to the radical anion as compared to four electrons to reduce it to phenylhydroxylamine.

It may seem strange that nitrosobenzene ϕNO is not found as an intermediate. In fact ϕNO is reduced much more easily than ϕNO_2 and hence is unstable at potentials where ϕNO_2 is reacting. Thus the two barriers to the reduction of ϕNO_2 are the first electron transfer and the breaking of a N—O bond.

The radical anion intermediate can be detected and measured not only using the electrochemical detection of the ring electrode but also using e.s.r.†

† Electron spin resonance. See McLauchlan's *Magnetic resonance* (OCS 1) for an account.

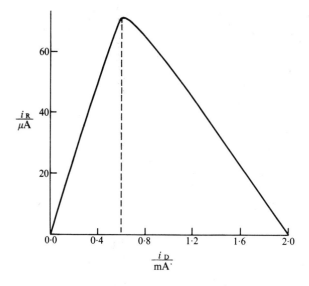

FIG. 5.17. Ring current for oxidation of ϕNO_2^- as a function of the disc current. Note that the maximum is at about $\frac{1}{4}$ of $i_{D,L}$ corresponding to 1 e$^-$ for ϕNO_2^- and 4 e$^-$ for $\phi NHOH$.

The experiment can be performed either by generating the radical outside the cavity and then flowing the solution into the cavity or by placing the electrode actually in the cavity. The second method is better suited for unstable radicals but has the disadvantage that the hydrodynamic characteristics of the electrode are not well defined. However the use of e.s.r. to detect radical intermediates in electro-organic reactions is an important and growing field.

Hammett plots

In physical organic chemistry linear free-energy relationships are used to correlate data,‡ and one of the most successful of these relationships is the Hammett σ/ρ plot for aromatic compounds. In this plot σ describes the effect of a *m*- or *p*-substituent X on the dissociation constant of the acid $X \cdot C_6 H_4 CO_2 H$,

$$\sigma = pK_{C_6H_5CO_2H} - pK_{XC_6H_4CO_2H}.$$

The more electron withdrawing is X the larger is the value of σ. The rates of many reactions are found to obey the relation

$$\log k_X = \log k_{X=H} + \sigma\rho.$$

‡ J. Shorter, *loc. cit.*

The parameter ρ is the gradient of the plot of $\log k_X$ against σ and describes how sensitive the reaction is to the supply of electrons from X.

Zuman has shown that many electrochemical rate constants for aromatic compounds also obey the Hammett Plot. In the electrochemical case since,

$$k'_E = k'_D \quad \text{at } E = E_{\frac{1}{2}},$$

and

$$k'_E = k'_{E=0} \exp\left(-\frac{\alpha E F}{RT}\right),$$

then

$$\log k'_{E=0} = \log k'_D + \frac{\alpha E_{\frac{1}{2}} F}{2 \cdot 3 R T}.$$

Hence for a constant value of k'_D (the transport to the electrode) and assuming that $\log k'_{E=0}$ obeys the Hammett relation, we find that

$$(E_{\frac{1}{2}})_X = (E_{\frac{1}{2}})_{X=H} + \frac{2 \cdot 3 R T}{\alpha F} \sigma \rho.$$

This elegant form of the Hammett relation has been found to hold for many systems including the reduction of nitrobenzene.

Fig. 5.18 shows a typical plot for the reduction of $X \cdot C_6H_4 \cdot CHO$ to $X \cdot C_6H_4 \cdot CH_2OH$ on a D.M.E. at pH 13. Remember that the more negative the $E_{\frac{1}{2}}$, the harder the reduction has to be driven to make it go and hence the slower the reaction. It will be seen that ρ is positive and that the more electron-withdrawing is X the easier it is to transfer an electron from the metal to the aromatic molecule. This is the general pattern for such reductions. If the point for $X = p\text{-}CHO$ is plotted against the normal σ, defined above, it lies well above the line. This is because for certain reactions with $p\text{-}CHO$ there can be a contribution from quinonoid structures. For example in our electrochemical case in the reduction of the radical

$$^-O-CH=\!\!\left\langle\underset{}{\bigcirc}\right\rangle\!\!=CH-O^{\cdot}$$

and in the dissociation for the phenol to the phenolate ion.

$$^-O-CH=\!\!\left\langle\underset{}{\bigcirc}\right\rangle\!\!=O$$

From the dissociation constant of the phenol a secondary σ^- value can be derived. When these values are used for the p groups (CHO, CN, and CO_2^-), which can have quinonoid contributions, they lie close to the line.

Zuman has collected together many examples of these linear free-energy relations. It is satisfactory that electro-organic reactions are as well-behaved

† P. Zuman, *Substitution effects in organic polarography*, Plenum Press, 1967.

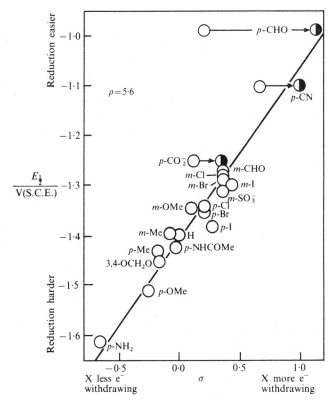

FIG. 5.18. Hammett plot for the reduction of XC_6H_4CHO on a Hg electrode at pH 13. The half-filled points are for *para*-groups which can form quinonoid hybrids and are the $E_{\frac{1}{2}}$ values plotted against σ^- rather than σ. Figure from P. Zuman, *Substituent effects in organic polarography*.

as the more traditional reactions of physical organic chemistry and that the same parameters can be used for both types of reaction.

Cyclic voltammetry

A useful technique for investigating the existence of intermediates in an electrochemical reaction is cyclic voltammetry. This technique can be done on a stationary electrode. The potential of the electrode is changed with time in a triangular wave form: it is increased at a constant rate up to a limit and then the direction of sweep is reversed. This is shown in Fig. 5.19a. The current is measured throughout the cycle and is plotted against the potential. The results in Fig. 5.19b are some obtained by Adams for 10^{-3} M Fe(III) in 1 M H_2SO_4 on Pt, at a sweep rate of 1 V min^{-1}. This is a simple one-electron system and one obtains two humps, one of Fe(III) to Fe(II) and the other for the reverse reaction. The product of one hump is the reactant for the next.

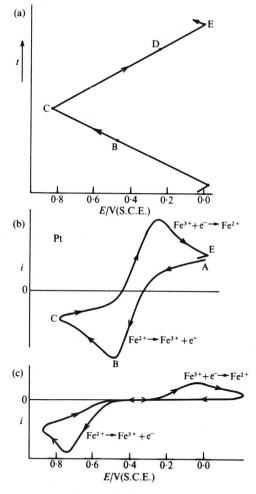

FIG. 5.19. Cyclic voltametry for Fe^{3+}/Fe^{2+} system. (a) Variation of potential with time which produces the current–voltage cycle shown in (b). On carbon paste electrode rates of reaction are slower and the humps are further apart as in (c). Data from R. N. Adams, *Electrochemistry at solid electrodes.*

The increasing part of each hump is caused by the electrode kinetics becoming favourable for the reaction. The decreasing part is caused by the reactant becoming depleted at the electrode surface.

If one carries out the cyclic voltammetry on a carbon paste electrode rather than platinum the humps become further apart as in Fig. 5.19c; the rates of reaction are slower on a carbon paste electrode and the system has to be driven harder. Quantitative information about the rates of reaction can be found by analysing the curves but the theory is fairly complicated.

Cyclic voltammetry is therefore probably most useful for qualitative investigations of multi-step systems; however, one can obtain semi-quantitative estimates of the lifetimes of intermediates. The sweep rate is an important variable. At fast sweep rates one may prove the existence of unstable intermediates which at slower sweep rates decompose before they can be observed.

Oxidation of aniline

A good example of the identification of different products from an electrochemical reaction by cyclic voltammetry is the oxidation of aniline in acid solution. Some of Adams and Bacon's results are given in Fig. 5.20. The whole reaction scheme may be written:

A

then either

B

or

P

The products benzidine (B) and amino diphenylamine (P) are themselves electrochemically active and so we have the further reactions:

B

$$+ 2H^+ + 2e^-$$

and

$$\text{(structures)} \quad P \rightleftharpoons Q + 2H^+ + 2e^-.$$

The labels in Fig. 5.20 show how this scheme explains the cyclic voltammetry.

Kolbe reaction and other dimerizations

The oxidation of aniline is an example of an important class of reactions in which electrogenerated radicals couple to form dimers. The Kolbe synthesis is another classical example:

$$RCO_2^- \rightarrow RCO_2^{\cdot} + e^-$$
$$RCO_2^{\cdot} \rightarrow R^{\cdot} + CO_2\uparrow$$
$$R^{\cdot} + R^{\cdot} \rightarrow R_2.$$

The carboxylate anions are oxidized at very high anodic potentials (~ 2 V). At this potential the solvent should decompose to give oxygen but due to adsorption the carboxylate oxidation must be kinetically favoured. When mixtures of anions are used cross products R^1R^2 can be made. The reaction does not work for aromatic anions (e.g. $C_6H_5CO_2^-$).

A selection of coupling reactions of this sort is collected in Table 5.5. In most cases the electrogenerated radicals are absorbed on the electrode and the overall mechanism for this type of reaction must be more complicated than the successive electron and proton transfer reactions discussed hitherto. One of the challenging problems of organic electrochemistry is to discover and understand the conditions which cause electrogenerated radicals to undergo a second electron transfer as opposed to coupling to form a dimer:

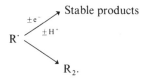

The coupling reactions in Table 5.5 are all oxidations. Coupling can also be achieved by reduction. An example of this type of process is the commercially-important production of adiponitrile, the nylon precursor, from

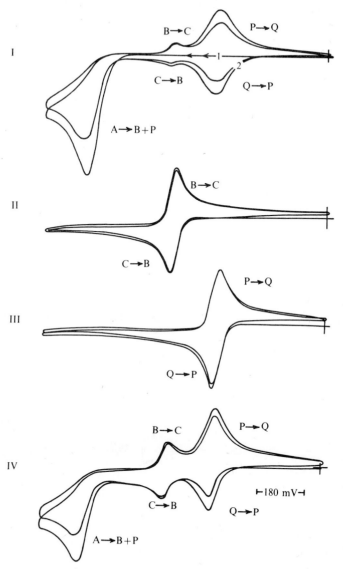

FIG. 5.20. Cyclic voltammetry for oxidation of aniline showing production of the two different electroactive products; I, aniline (A) alone; (II) benzidine (B) alone; III, p-amino-diphenylamine (P) alone; IV mixture of A, B and P. Note that on first scan (1) of aniline no product peaks are seen since no C or Q are formed until after the first excursion round the A hairpins.

TABLE 5.5

Examples of coupling reactions†

$$CH_3[CH_2]_nCO_2^- \xrightarrow{-e^-,\ -CO_2} CH_3[CH_2]_n\!\cdot \longrightarrow CH_3[CH_2]_{2n}CH_3$$
$$n = 0\text{-}14$$

$$CH_3-C{=}CH-CO_2Et \xrightarrow{-e^-} CH_3-\overset{\displaystyle O}{C}-\overset{\displaystyle \cdot}{CH}-CO_2Et \longrightarrow \begin{array}{c} CH_3COCH-CO_2Et \\ CH_3COCH-CO_2Et \end{array}$$
(enolate with O^-)

$$\underset{\displaystyle O^-}{\overset{\displaystyle O^-}{(CH_3)_2C{=}N^+}} \xrightarrow{-e^-} \underset{\displaystyle O^-}{\overset{\displaystyle O^-}{(CH_3)_2\overset{\cdot}{C}-N^+}} \longrightarrow \begin{array}{c} (CH_3)_2C-NO_2 \\ (CH_3)_2C-NO_2 \end{array}$$

$$(CH_3)_2COH-C{\equiv}C^- \xrightarrow{-e^-} (CH_3)_2COH-C{\equiv}C\!\cdot \longrightarrow ((CH_3)_2COH-C{\equiv}C-)_2$$

$$CH_3CH_2S^- \xrightarrow{-e^-} CH_3CH_2S\!\cdot \longrightarrow \begin{array}{c} CH_3CH_2-S \\ CH_3CH_2-S \end{array}$$

$$C_6H_5MgBr \xrightarrow{-e^-,\ -MgBr} C_6H_5\!\cdot \longrightarrow C_6H_5{-}C_6H_5$$

$$O_2N{-}\!\!\!\bigcirc\!\!\!{-}NH_2 \xrightarrow{-e^-} O_2N{-}\!\!\!\bigcirc\!\!\!{-}\overset{+}{N}H_2\!\cdot \xrightarrow{-2H^+} O_2N{-}\!\!\!\bigcirc\!\!\!{-}NH{-}NH{-}\!\!\!\bigcirc\!\!\!{-}NO_2$$

$$\xrightarrow{-2e^-\ -2H^+} O_2N{-}\!\!\!\bigcirc\!\!\!{-}N{=}N{-}\!\!\!\bigcirc\!\!\!{-}NO_2$$

$$\bigcirc\!\!\!{-}NH_2 \xrightarrow{-e^-} \bigcirc\!\!\!{-}\overset{+}{N}H_2\!\cdot \longrightarrow \text{see above}$$

$$CH_3{-}\!\!\!\bigcirc\!\!\!{-}OH \xrightarrow{-e^-} CH_3{-}\!\!\!\bigcirc\!\!\!{-}\overset{+}{O}H\!\cdot \xrightarrow{-2H^+} \text{(coupled bisphenol: } CH_3,\ OH,\ OH,\ CH_3\text{)}$$

acrylonitrile:

$$CH_2=CH-CN \xrightarrow{e^-} {}^-CH_2-CH-CN$$

$${}^-CH_2-\overset{\cdot}{C}H-CN + CH_2=CH-CN$$
$$\downarrow{H^+}$$
$$NC\overset{\cdot}{C}HCH_2CH_2CH_2CN$$
$$\downarrow{e^-,\,H^+}$$
$$NCCH_2CH_2CH_2CH_2CN.$$

This mechanism is a mixture of the coupling and the successive type. This book is too short to review all the complexities of organic electrochemistry; but readers can find an excellent survey in Eberson and Schäfer's monograph.[†] Table 5.5 can only serve as an *hors d'ouvre* to whet the appetite. The variety of reactions, their synthetic utility and their mechanistic interest promise a full and interesting life to the young science of electro-organic chemistry and this despite the mutual suspicion and incomprehension of its two parent disciplines.

Reduction of O_2 at Hg

We finish with an example that illustrates the importance of adsorption in electrochemical processes. Gierst and Lambert have studied the reduction of O_2 on a mercury surface in the presence of α and β-quinolines. In 1 mol dm^{-3} NaOH the first stage of the reduction is a two-electron reduction to HO_2^- the conjugate base of H_2O_2. The first one-electron step is rate determining:

$$O_2 + e^- \rightarrow O_2^{\cdot-} \qquad \text{Rate-determining step}$$
$$O_2^{\cdot-} + H_2O + e^- \rightarrow HO_2^- + OH^- \qquad \text{Fast}$$

A simple irreversible wave is observed as shown in Fig. 5.21. At more reducing potentials a second two-electron wave corresponding to the reduction,

$$HO_2^- + 2e^- + H_2O \rightarrow 3OH^-$$

is found, but this second wave does not concern us.

In the presence of a saturated solution of α-quinoline, the shape of the wave is grossly altered as shown in Fig. 5.21. Instead of one two-electron wave, two one-electron waves are found. An adsorbed layer of the quinoline completely changes the kinetics of the electrode surface, somewhat slowing down the first electron transfer and very much decreasing the rate of the second electron transfer so that $O_2^{\cdot-}$ is no longer destroyed on the electrode, giving

$$O_2 + e^- \rightarrow O_2^{\cdot-} \qquad \text{First wave}$$
$$O_2^{\cdot-} + e^- + H_2O \rightarrow HO_2^- + OH^-. \qquad \text{Second wave}$$

† L. Eberson and H. Schäfer, *Organic electrochemistry*, Springer-Verlag, 1971.

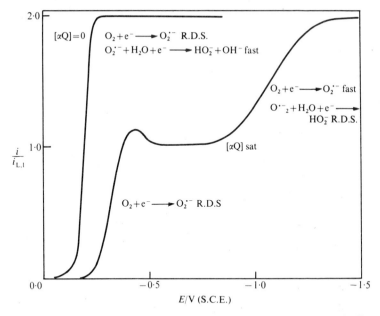

FIG. 5.21. The reduction of oxygen on mercury at pH 14. In the absence of quinolines one two-electron wave is seen (Case I), in a saturated solution of α quinoline two one-electron waves are found (Case IIA). Data from L. Gierst and J. Lambert.

With the β-quinoline, an even more surprising wave is found as shown in Fig. 5.22. At potentials less reducing than -760 mV the behaviour is the same as the α-quinoline with the first wave due to

$$O_2 + e^- \rightarrow O_2^-$$

being observed. But at -760 mV this current completely collapses to a value indistinguishable from the background current in the absence of O_2. The electrode reaction is completely switched off. Eventually at more reducing potentials a two-electron wave is observed. The dramatic switch-off is caused by a change in the packing in the adsorbed layer. To start with at the less negative potentials both quinoline molecules lie flat on the electrode, but at more negative potentials the strong field at the electrode causes the negatively-charged nitrogens to get as far from the surface as possible; the molecules pack on their edges, in two different ways depending on the isomer. In the case of the β-quinoline this type of packing completely blocks the electrode reaction. At the potential where the switch off takes place the capacitance of the electrode also shows a discontinuity as the β-quinoline changes its packing.

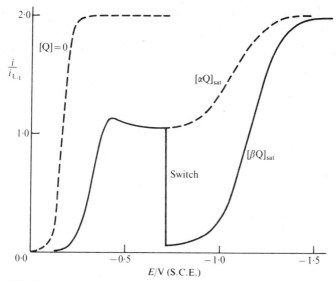

FIG. 5.22. The reduction of oxygen on mercury at pH 14 in a saturated solution of β-quinoline. The broken lines are the curves in Fig. 5.21. Data from L. Gierst and J. Lambert.

We started with the effect of the potential on the straightforward rate of reaction. We end with the potential operating a molecular switch. In a book of this length this last example can only be a cautionary tale about the effects of adsorption. But the application of modern physical techniques such as e.s.r., reflectance spectroscopy, photochemical generation, mass spectrometry, and ellipsometry to the detailed studies of electrochemical reactions should mean that today's cautionary tales become tomorrow's text books.

Appendix 1. Detailed solution of Poisson–Boltzmann equation

FROM eqn (2.10) we have to solve

$$\frac{\partial^2 \theta}{\partial \chi^2} = \tfrac{1}{2} \sinh(2\theta)$$

where at $\chi = 0$, $\theta = \theta_0$ and as $\chi \to \infty$, $\theta \to 0$.

We multiply each side by $2\,d\theta/d\chi$ and then integrate with respect to χ to give

$$\left(\frac{d\theta}{d\chi}\right)^2 = \tfrac{1}{2}\cosh(2\theta) + \text{integration constant}$$

$$= \tfrac{1}{2}[\cosh(2\theta) - 1]$$

$$= \sinh^2(\theta). \tag{A1.1}$$

The evaluation of the integration constant arises from the fact that when $x \to \infty$ both ϕ_Δ and $d\phi_\Delta/dx$ tend to zero. This can be seen in Fig. 2.4. In terms of θ and χ, when $\chi \to \infty$, θ and $d\theta/d\chi$ both tend to zero.

Taking the square root of either side we obtain

$$\frac{d\theta}{d\chi} = -\sinh\theta. \tag{A1.2}$$

We have to take the negative root for θ to decay to zero at large values of χ: when θ is positive $d\theta/d\chi$ must be negative and vice versa. This again can be seen in Fig. 2.4.

Using the standard integral,

$$\int \operatorname{cosech}\theta = \ln(\tanh\tfrac{1}{2}\theta),$$

we integrate (A1.2) to obtain

$$\chi = \ln\left[\frac{\tanh\tfrac{1}{2}\theta_0}{\tanh\tfrac{1}{2}\theta}\right] \tag{A1.3}$$

or

$$\tanh\tfrac{1}{2}\theta = (\tanh\tfrac{1}{2}\theta_0)\exp(-\chi).$$

The integration constant is determined by the fact that $\theta = \theta_0$ at $\chi = 0$.

In this appendix we also work out the integral needed in eqn (2.17) for calculating the capacitance of the diffuse double layer.

Using eqn (A1.2) we obtain

$$\int_0^\infty \sinh(2\theta)\,d\chi = \int_{\theta_0}^0 \frac{\sinh(2\theta)}{\sinh(\theta)}\,d\theta = -\int_0^{\theta_0} 2\cosh\theta\,d\theta = -2\sinh\theta_0.$$

Appendix 2. The Lippmann equation

To interpret the measurements of γ versus E we have to consider the free energy of the charged interface, A_H^σ. For a surface we can write

$$\mathrm{d}A_H^\sigma = \gamma \, \mathrm{d}A - S^\sigma \, \mathrm{d}T + \Sigma \mu \, \mathrm{d}n^\sigma + \Delta\phi \, \mathrm{d}Q_M \qquad (A2.1)$$

where

$$\Delta\phi = \phi_M - \phi_S.$$

The first three terms may be compared with the more familiar

$$\mathrm{d}A_H = -P \, \mathrm{d}V - S \, \mathrm{d}T + \Sigma \mu \, \mathrm{d}n.$$

The term $\gamma \, \mathrm{d}A$ describes the reversible work from the expansion or contraction of the interface (cf. $P \, \mathrm{d}V$). The terms $S \, \mathrm{d}T$ and $\mu \, \mathrm{d}n^\sigma$ need no comment except to point out that n^σ measures the difference in concentration at the interface compared to the bulk values. The term $\Delta\phi \, \mathrm{d}Q_M$ arises from the reversible electrical work that can be done in charging or discharging the interface which has a total charge of Q_M. Since we work at constant T we can drop the $S^\sigma \, \mathrm{d}T$ term. Then consider increasing the size of the interface under conditions of constant γ, μ and $\Delta\phi$; by integration from $A_H^\sigma = 0$ we obtain

$$A_H^\sigma = \gamma A + \Sigma \mu n^\sigma + \Delta\phi Q_M.$$

Differentiation and application of (A2.1) gives

$$0 = A \, \mathrm{d}\gamma + \Sigma n^\sigma \, \mathrm{d}\mu + Q_M \, \mathrm{d}\Delta\phi.$$

Now in the electrocapillary experiments the chemical potentials of all the components remain constant, and so we obtain the *Lippmann equation*

$$\left(\frac{\partial \gamma}{\partial \Delta\phi} \right)_{T, A_H, \mu} = -\frac{Q_M}{A}.$$

Appendix 3. Effect of double-layer correction on reaction order and transfer coefficient

FROM eqn (2.25),

$$\text{rate}_{O \to R} = (k_1')_{\phi_M = \phi_1} \exp \left[-\frac{\alpha_1 F \Delta\phi}{RT} \right] f_{DL}[O]_* \qquad (A3.1)$$

where from eqn (2.27)

$$f_{DL} = \exp \left[2(\alpha_1 - Z_0)\theta_H \right]. \qquad (A3.2)$$

For the order of the reaction by definition

$$m_0 = \frac{\partial \ln (\text{rate})}{\partial \ln [O]_*} = 1 + \left(\frac{\partial \ln f_{DL}}{\partial \ln [O]_*} \right)_{\Delta\phi}$$

$$= 1 + 2(\alpha_1 - Z_0)\frac{\partial \theta_H}{\partial \ln [O]_*}. \qquad (A3.3)$$

In the last two steps we have substituted from (A3.1) and (A3.2). The term $\partial \theta_H / \partial \ln [O]_*$ describes the effect of changes in the electrolyte concentration on the distribution of potential in the double layer. To calculate this distribution exactly we cannot use the differential capacities C' because from (2.19) the capacitance of the diffuse double layer is itself a function of the potential difference:

$$C'_{DL} = C'_{DL,0} \cosh (\theta_H).$$

In charging up the diffuse double layer from $\theta_H = 0$ we can write

$$dq = C'_{DL} \, d\phi_H = \frac{2RT}{zF} C'_{DL} \, d\theta_H = \frac{2RT}{zF} C'_{DL,0} \cosh \theta_H \, d\theta_H.$$

Integration gives

$$q = \frac{2RT}{zF} C'_{DL,0} \sinh \theta_H.$$

We can now define the integral capacity per unit area of the diffuse double layer $\mathscr{C}'_{DL}$ where

$$q = \mathscr{C}'_{DL}\phi_H = \frac{2RT}{zF} \mathscr{C}'_{DL}\theta_H.$$

Hence

$$\mathscr{C}'_{DL} = C'_{DL,0} \frac{\sinh \theta_H}{\theta_H}.$$

The distribution of the potential is governed by the integral rather than the differential capacities.

Thus

$$\theta_H = \frac{\mathscr{C}'_H}{\mathscr{C}'_H + \mathscr{C}'_{DL}}\theta_0.$$

Rearranging and substituting for $\mathscr{C}'_{DL}$ and for $\mathscr{C}'_H$—under the assumption that C'_H is constant $\mathscr{C}'_H = C'_H$—we obtain

$$\theta_0 = \theta_H + \frac{C'_{DL,0}\sinh\theta_H}{C'_H}.$$

Differentiation gives

$$d\theta_0 = d\theta_H + \frac{C'_{DL,0}}{C'_H}(\cosh\theta_H\, d\theta_H + \sinh\theta_H\, d\ln C'_{DL,0}). \qquad (A3.4)$$

From (2.20) $C'_{DL,0} \propto c_*^{\frac{1}{2}}$ and for constant θ_0 and varying $[O]_*$ we obtain

$$\frac{\partial\theta_H}{\partial\ln[O]_*} = -\frac{1}{2}\left(\frac{\sinh\theta_H}{C'_H/C'_{DL,0} + \cosh\theta_H}\right).$$

Substitution in (8.3) gives

$$m_0 = 1 + \frac{(z_0 - \alpha_1)C'_{DL,0}\sinh\theta_H}{C'_H + C'_{DL,0}\cosh\theta_H}.$$

Now we turn to the effect on the transfer coefficient. From the definition of α in (1.20) and from (A3.1)

$$\alpha = \alpha_1 - \frac{RT}{F}\left(\frac{\partial\ln f_{DL}}{\partial\Delta\phi}\right)_{[O]_*}$$

$$= \alpha_1 - \frac{1}{2}\left(\frac{\partial\ln f_{DL}}{\partial\theta_0}\right)_{[O]_*}.$$

Using (A3.2)

$$\alpha = \alpha_1 + (z_0 - \alpha_1)\left(\frac{\partial\theta_H}{\partial\theta_0}\right)_{[O]_*}.$$

Substituting from (8.4), where at constant $[O]_*$, $C'_{DL,0}$ is constant,

$$\alpha = \alpha_1 + \frac{(z_0 - \alpha_1)}{1 + (C'_{DL,0}/C'_H)\cosh(\theta_H)}.$$

Appendix 4. Solution of Levich equation for transport to R.D.E.

WE have to solve (3.4)

$$D\frac{\partial^2 c}{\partial x^2} = v_x\frac{\partial c}{\partial x} \qquad\qquad (A4.1)$$

with the boundary condition

$$x \to \infty, \qquad c \to c_\infty.$$

From (3.2)

$$v_x = -(\omega v)^{\frac{1}{2}} X(x/x_{Hy})$$
$$\simeq -C_\omega x^2, \qquad\qquad (A4.2)$$

when

$$x < 0.2x_{Hy},$$

and where

$$C_\omega = 0.510\omega^{\frac{3}{2}}v^{-\frac{1}{2}}. \qquad\qquad (A4.3)$$

Here we have approximated for the function X for low values of x. We shall show later that this approximation is justified.

Eqn (9.1) now becomes

$$D\frac{\partial^2 c}{\partial x^2} = -C_\omega x^2\frac{\partial c}{\partial x}.$$

Let

$$\chi = xC_\omega^{\frac{1}{3}}D^{-\frac{1}{3}}, \qquad\qquad (A4.4)$$

then

$$\frac{\partial^2 c}{\partial \chi^2} = -\chi^2\frac{\partial c}{\partial \chi}.$$

Multiply by $\exp\left(-\frac{1}{3}\chi^3\right)$ and integrate to obtain

$$\frac{\partial c}{\partial \chi} = \left(\frac{\partial c}{\partial \chi}\right)_{\chi=0}\exp\left(-\frac{1}{3}\chi^3\right).$$

Integrate this equation again to give

$$c = c_0 + \left(\frac{\partial c}{\partial \chi}\right)_{\chi=0}\int_0^x \exp\left(-\frac{1}{3}\lambda^3\right)d\lambda. \qquad\qquad (A4.5)$$

This equation describes the complete concentration profile of c as a function of χ and is plotted in Fig. 3.8. In particular as $\chi \to \infty$ and we reach the bulk of the solution

$$c_\infty = c_0 + \left(\frac{\partial c}{\partial \chi}\right)_{\chi = 0} \int_0^\infty \exp\left(-\tfrac{1}{3}\lambda^3\right) \mathrm{d}\lambda.$$

The definite integral can be evaluated and is equal to $3^{\frac{1}{3}}\Gamma(1\tfrac{1}{3}) = 1\cdot288$. Hence

$$1\cdot288\left(\frac{\partial c}{\partial \chi}\right)_{\chi = 0} = c_\infty - c_0. \tag{A4.6}$$

Now we define, using (A4.3) and (A4.4),

$$x_\mathrm{D} = 1\cdot288 x/\chi = 1\cdot288 D^{\frac{1}{3}} C_\omega^{-\frac{1}{2}}$$
$$= 0\cdot643 W^{-\frac{1}{2}} v^{\frac{1}{6}} D^{\frac{1}{3}} \tag{A4.7}$$

where W is the rotation speed measured in Hz and $x = x_\mathrm{D}$ when $\chi = 1\cdot288$. Then substitution in (A4.6) gives

$$\left(\frac{\partial c}{\partial x}\right)_{x = 0} = \frac{c_\infty - c_0}{x_\mathrm{D}}. \tag{A4.8}$$

Appendix 5. Solution to Ilkovic equation

THE differential eqn (3.33) is

$$\frac{\partial c}{\partial t} = D\frac{\partial^2 c}{\partial x^2}$$

with boundary conditions

$$t = 0 \qquad c = c_\infty$$

$$x \to \infty \qquad c \to c_\infty$$

$$x = 0 \qquad c = 0.$$

The solution given in (3.34) is

$$c = \frac{2c_\infty}{\sqrt{\pi}}\int_0^{x/2\sqrt{(Dt)}} \exp(-\lambda^2)\,d\lambda = c_\infty \operatorname{erf}\frac{x}{2\sqrt{(Dt)}}.$$

Now $\int_0^\infty e^{-\lambda^2}\,d\lambda = \tfrac{1}{2}\sqrt{\pi}$. So when either $x \to \infty$ or $t \to 0$,

$$\frac{x}{2\sqrt{(Dt)}} \to \infty \quad \text{and} \quad c \to c_\infty.$$

Hence the solution obeys the boundary conditions.
   Differentiating,

$$\frac{\partial c}{\partial t} = \frac{2c_\infty}{\sqrt{\pi}}\cdot\exp\left(-\frac{x^2}{4Dt}\right)\cdot\left[\frac{-x}{4D^{\frac{1}{2}}t^{\frac{3}{2}}}\right],$$

$$\frac{\partial c}{\partial x} = \frac{2c_\infty}{\sqrt{\pi}}\cdot\exp\left(\frac{-x^2}{4Dt}\right)\cdot\frac{1}{2\sqrt{(Dt)}}, \qquad\qquad \text{(A5.1)}$$

and

$$\frac{\partial^2 c}{\partial x^2} = \frac{2c_\infty}{\sqrt{\pi}}\cdot\exp\left(\frac{-x^2}{4Dt}\right)\cdot\frac{1}{2\sqrt{(Dt)}}\cdot\left[\frac{-2x}{4Dt}\right] = \frac{1}{D}\frac{\partial c}{\partial t}.$$

Thus the solution also obeys the differential equation.

Appendix 6. Current–voltage characteristics of electrode network

GIVEN an alternating potential across a network of the form

$$E = E_m \cos(\omega't),$$

the current will not necessarily be in phase with the voltage but will be displaced in time as shown in Fig. 3.32. We can write the current as

$$i = \frac{E_m}{Z} \cos(\omega't + p) \tag{A6.1}$$

where p describes the phase shift—that is the difference in radians between the maximum in the current and the maximum in the potential, (see Fig. 3.32); Z is the impedance and the maximum current and maximum voltage are related by

$$i_m = E_m/Z,$$

but i_m and E_m are not observed at the same point in time unless $p = 0$.

The current can also be expressed as

$$i = \frac{E_m}{R_X^2 + R_Y^2}[R_X \cos(\omega't) - R_Y \sin(\omega't)]. \tag{A6.2}$$

Differentiation to find the maximum gives

$$\frac{di}{dt} = \frac{E_m\omega'}{(R_X^2 + R_Y^2)}[-R_X \sin(\omega't) - R_Y \cos(\omega't)] = 0.$$

Hence the maximum occurs when

$$\tan(\omega't) = -\frac{R_Y}{R_X}$$

or

$$-\omega't = \tan^{-1}(R_Y/R_X)$$

Comparison with (A6.1) shows that

$$p = \tan^{-1}(R_Y/R_X)$$

Substitution in (A6.2) gives

$$i_m = E_m/\sqrt{(R_X^2 + R_Y^2)}.$$

Hence

$$Z = \sqrt{(R_X^2 + R_Y^2)}.$$

Fig. A6.1 shows a geometrical construction which shows the relations between Z, p, R_X, and R_Y. The diagram is similar to the Argand diagram and the

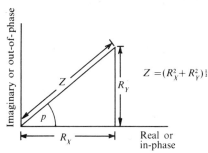

FIG. A6.1. Argand diagram showing relations between Z, p, R_x and R_y and how the impedance may be expressed as the complex number $Z' = R_x + iR_y$.

information can be written as a complex number in the form

$$Z' = R_X + iR_Y, \qquad (A6.3)$$

where

$$i = \sqrt{(-1)}.$$

The advantage of doing this is that in calculating the impedance of complicated networks Z' obeys the same rules as simple resistances. Therefore to work out the characteristics of the following network,

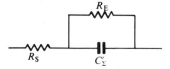

we first write down Z'_c for the capacitance:

$$E_c = \frac{1}{C'_E} \int i_c \, dt$$

or for $E_c = E_{c,m} \cos \omega' t$

$$i_c = -\omega' C_\Sigma E_{c,m} \sin \omega' t$$

and

$$Z' = i(\omega' C_\Sigma)^{-1}.$$

Now treating the resistance and capacitance in parallel

$$\frac{1}{Z'_{E,\Sigma}} = \frac{1}{Z'_E} + \frac{1}{Z'_\Sigma} = \frac{1}{R_E} - i\omega' C_\Sigma$$

or

$$Z'_{E,\Sigma} = \frac{R_E}{1 - \omega' C_\Sigma R_E i} = \frac{R_E + i\omega' C_\Sigma R_E^2}{1 + (\omega' C_\Sigma R_E)^2}. \qquad (A6.4)$$

For the whole combination

$$Z' = R_S + Z'_{E.\Sigma}.$$ (A6.5)

From (A6.4) and equating the real and imaginary parts between (A6.3) and (A6.5) we obtain

$$R_X = R_S + \frac{R_E}{1 + (\omega' C_\Sigma R_E)^2}$$

and

$$R_Y = \frac{\omega' C_\Sigma R_E^2}{1 + (\omega' C_\Sigma R_E)^2}.$$

Appendix 7. The Levich–Marcus theory

IN this appendix we work out the activation energy in terms of the thermo-dynamic parameters for two intersecting parabolas. The necessary coordinate geometry is shown in Fig. A7.1.

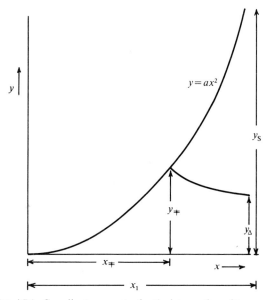

FIG. A7.1. Coordinate geometry for the intersection of two parabolas.

Then firstly $y_S = ax_1^2$ and secondly

$$y = y_\ddagger = ax_\ddagger^2 = y_\Delta + a(x_\ddagger - x_1)^2$$
$$= y_\Delta + ax_\ddagger^2 - 2ax_1x_\ddagger + ax_1^2.$$

So

$$2ax_1x_\ddagger = y_\Delta + ax_1^2 = y_\Delta + y_S$$

Then dividing by $2ax_1^2 = 2y_S$ we obtain

$$\frac{x_\ddagger}{x_1} = \frac{y_\Delta + y_S}{2y_S}$$

Hence

$$y_\ddagger = ax_\ddagger^2 = ax_1^2 \frac{(y_\Delta + y_S)^2}{4y_S^2} = \frac{(y_\Delta + y_S)^2}{4y_S}.$$

Appendix 8. The Koutecky–Levich equation

IN this appendix we derive the exponential form of the imbalance in the equilibrium for the weak acid system:

Solution

$$HA \underset{k_{-1}}{\overset{k_1}{\rightleftharpoons}} H^+ + A^-$$

Electrode

$$H^+ + e^- \longrightarrow \tfrac{1}{2}H_2.$$

From (5.12)

$$c' = \frac{K_A}{c_A} c_{HA} - c_H$$

where

$$\text{as } x \to \infty \qquad c' \to 0 \tag{A8.1}$$

and at

$$x = 0 \qquad c' = c'_0 = K_A c_{HA,0}/c_A. \tag{A8.2}$$

Now in (5.6) and (5.7) we can write

$$k_1 c_{HA} - k_{-1} c_A c_H = k_{-1} c_A c'.$$

Multiply (5.6) by $K_A/(c_A D_{HA})$ and (5.7) by D_H^{-1} and subtract to obtain

$$\frac{\partial^2 \{(K_A c_{HA}/c_A) - c_H\}}{\partial x^2} = \frac{\partial^2 c'}{\partial x^2} = \left(\frac{K_A}{c_A D_{HA}} + \frac{1}{D_H} \right) k_{-1} c c'.$$

But because $K_A/c_A \ll 1$ we can ignore the K_A term and so

$$\frac{\partial^2 c'}{\partial x^2} \simeq \frac{k_{-1} c_A}{D_H} c'.$$

Integrating with the boundary conditions we find

$$c' = c'_0 \exp(-x/x_R)$$

where

$$x_R = \sqrt{\left(\frac{D_H}{k_{-1} c_A} \right)}.$$

Bibliography

General

K. J. VETTER, *Electrochemical kinetics*, Academic Press, 1967. A Rolls–Royce textbook (and about as expensive).

J. KORYTA, J. DVOŘÁK, and V. BOHÁČKOVÁ, *Electrochemistry*, Methuen, 1970. A very good general text book for first degree students.

J. O'M. BOCKRIS and A. K. N. REDDY, *Modern electrochemistry* (vols 1 and 2), Macdonald, 1970. Lively and entertaining gospel according to electrochemistry's leading evangelist.

N. S. HUSH (ed), *Reactions of molecules at electrodes*, Wiley, 1971. A collection of first-rate articles with a physical bias.

H. EYRING, D. HENDERSON, and W. JOST (eds), *Physical chemistry* (vols 9A and 9B), Academic Press, 1970. Vol. 9A contains articles by experts on the principles; 9B is more concerned with applications. The treatment is more suitable for graduates than for undergraduates.

G. J. HILLS, *Essays in chemistry*, 1971, **2**, 19.

K. J. LAIDLER, *J. chem. Educ.* 1970, **47**, 600. Two good introductory articles.

Double layer

D. GRAHAME, *Chem. Rev.*, 1947, **41**, 441. A classic article on the structure of the double layer.

R. PARSONS, *Advances in electrochemistry and electrochemical engineering*, 1961, **1**, 34. Deals clearly with the effect of the double layer on electrode kinetics.

C. A. BARLOW JR., *Physical chemistry* vol. 9A (ed. H. Eyring, D. Henderson, and W. Jost), ch. 2, Academic Press, 1970.

N. V. NIKOLAEVA-FEDEROVICH, B. N. RYBAKOV, and K. A. RADYUSHKINA, *Soviet electrochemistry*, 1967, **3**, 967. More results and discussion from Frumkin's group on the $S_2O_8^{2-}$ system discussed in Chapter 2.

Techniques

V. G. LEVICH, *Physicochemical hydrodynamics*, Prentice Hall, 1962. A *magnum opus* which deals with many chemical problems involving fluid flow.

R. N. ADAMS, *Electrochemistry at solid electrodes*, Dekker, 1969. A good no-nonsense approach. Includes a valuable survey of electro-organic reactions.

A. C. RIDDIFORD, *Advances in electrochemistry and electrochemical engineering*, 1965, **4**, 47. Definitive article on rotating disc system.

P. DELAHAY, *New instrumental methods in electrochemistry*, Interscience, 1954. Not so new now but this is the only criticism.

B. B. DAMASKIN, *The principles of current methods for the study of electrochemical reactions*, McGraw-Hill, 1967. A lucid and well written account, by a leading Soviet electrochemist, of many different techniques.

H. R. THIRSK and J. A. HARRISON. *A guide to the study of electrode kinetics*, Academic Press, 1972. A handbook containing equations for many different techniques and reaction schemes, with an interesting chapter on surfaces.

W. J. ALBERY and M. L. HITCHMAN, *Ring disc electrodes*, Clarendon Press, 1971. A competent survey, which has been properly criticized for not containing enough of the Russian work.

Marcus–Levich theory

V. G. LEVICH, *Advan. electrochem. electrochem. engng.*, 1966, **4**, 249.
R. A. MARCUS, *Electrochim Acta*, 1968, *B*, 995.
R. R. DOGONADZE, *Reactions of molecules at electrodes* (ed. N. S. Hush), Wiley, 1971, p. 135.
J. M. HALE, *Reactions of molecules at electrodes* (ed. N. S. Hush), Wiley, 1971, p. 229.

Electrolyte solutions

R. A. ROBINSON and R. H. STOKES, *Electrolyte solutions*, Butterworth, 1959.
H. S. HARNED and B. B. OWEN, *The physical chemistry of electrolytic solutions*, Reinhold, 1958.

Review articles

Good articles reviewing current developments are to be found in the following three series:
Modern aspects of electrochemistry, (ed. J. O'M. Bockris and B. E. Conway), Butterworths;
Electroanalytical chemistry (ed. A. J. Bard), Dekker;
Advances in electrochemistry and electrochemical engineering (ed. P. Delahay and C. W. Tobias), Interscience.

Other topics

E. F. CALDIN, *Fast reactions in solution*, Blackwell, 1964. Unfortunately out of print, but let us hope that before long we shall be given a second edition of this excellent book.
L. EBERSON and H. SCHÄFER, *Organic electrochemistry. Topics in current chemistry*, **21**, Springer-Verlag, 1971. A first-class systematic survey of reactions and mechanisms in organic electrochemistry.
P. ZUMAN, *Substituent effects in organic polarography*, Plenum, 1967. Systematic treatment of data in terms of linear free-energy relations.
W. VIELSTICH, *Fuel cells*, Interscience, 1970.
G. K. MANN and K. K. BARNES, *Electrochemical reactions in nonaqueous systems*, Dekker, 1970.
Intermediates in electrochemical reactions. Faraday Discussions, Butterworth, 1974. Papers on many new physical techniques applied to electrochemical reactions.
D. R. CROW, *Polarography of metal complexes*, Academic Press, 1969. A very competent survey of inorganic systems studied at the D.M.E.
M. W. BREITER, *Electrochemical processes in fuel cells*, Springer-Verlag, 1969.

Index

List of symbols

a	Ionic size parameter in Debye–Hückel theory
a	[A]
A	Area of electrode
A_H	Helmholtz free energy
b	[B]
B	Constant in Levich equation (eqn 3.15)
c	Concentration of a species
c	[C]
c'	Describes relaxation of equilibrium near electrode surface (eqn 5.12)
c_0	Concentration at electrode surface
c_*	Concentration just outside the double layer
c_∞	Concentration in bulk of solution
C_ω	Convection constant for R.D.E. (eqn A4.3)
C_B	Capacitance in Wheatstone Bridge
C_Σ	Overall capacitance of electrode
C'_{DL}	Differential capacitance per unit area of diffuse double layer
$C'_{DL,0}$	Differential capacitance per unit area of diffuse double layer at potential of zero charge
C'_H	Differential capacitance per unit area of Helmholtz layer
C'_Σ	Overall differential capacitance per unit area of the double layer
$\mathscr{C}'_{DL}$	Integral capacitance per unit area of diffuse double layer
$\mathscr{C}'_H$	Integral capacitance per unit area of Helmholtz layer
D	Diffusion coefficient
e	Charge of the electron
E	A measured potential difference across a cell
E_m	Maximum applied potential in alternating current experiments
E_{zc}	Potential of zero charge
E_0	Potential at which $i = 0$
$E_{\frac{1}{2}}$	Half wave potential
$E^\ominus$	Standard electrode potential
E'	$E - E^\ominus$
E_η	$E - E_0$ the overpotential
f_{DL}	Double layer correction function
F	Faraday
g	Gravitational constant
G_S	Change in solvation free energy
G_Δ	Change in free energy between Q and P
$G_\ddagger$	Free energy of activation for Q to P
$G^\ominus$	Standard Gibbs free energy
$\Delta G_P^\ominus$	Standard free energy change for forming P from products

$\Delta G_Q^{\ominus}$	Standard free energy change for forming Q from reactants
$\Delta G_{TD}^{\ominus}$	Overall standard free change for reaction
h	Planck's constant
h	Height of mercury column for a mercury electrode
$\Delta H_{\ddagger}^{\ominus}$	Standard enthalpy of activation
I	Current
i_C	Current corrected for concentration polarization
i_L	Transport limited current
i_0	Standard exchange current density
i	$\sqrt{(-1)}$
j	Flux
j_D	Flux on disc electrode
j_L	Transport limited flux
j_0	Transport limited flux for 0
j_R	Transport limited flux for R
j_R	Flux on ring electrode
j_0	Flux at $t = 0$ in potential step
k	Homogeneous rate constant
k'	Heterogeneous rate constant
k_B	Boltzmann constant
k_n'	Heterogeneous rate constant for nth step on electrode surface
k_D'	Heterogeneous rate constant describing mass transport
k_R'	Heterogeneous rate constant describing effect of homogeneous reaction in reaction layer (eqn 5.17)
k_0	Rate constant for zeroth level
k_0'	Value of k' at $E = E^{\ominus}$
k_2	Second order rate constant for homogeneous electron transfer
k_{Σ}	Rate constant for all levels
$\overleftarrow{k'}$	Observed heterogeneous rate constant in reducing direction
$\overrightarrow{k'}$	Observed heterogeneous rate constant in oxidising direction
K_E'	Equilibrium constant for locating reactant near electrode
K_P	Equilibrium constant for forming P from products
K_Q	Equilibrium constant for forming Q from reactants
K_{ε}	$\varepsilon/\varepsilon_0$ relative permittivity (used to be the dielectric constant)
m_{Hg}'	Rate of flow of Hg in a D.M.E. in kg s^{-1}
m_X	Order of electrochemical reaction with respect to species X.
n	Number of electrons consumed or released in an electrochemical reaction
N_i	Number of ith ions per unit volume
O	The oxidized species in a typical electrochemical reaction
p	Phase shift in a.c. experiment
P	Product complex
q	Charge per unit area
q_M	Charge per unit area on the metal

q_P	Molecular partition function of product
q_R	Molecular partition function of reactant
q_S	Charge per unit area in the solution
$q_{\ddagger}$	Molecular partition function of transition state
Q	Reactant complex
Q_M	Total charge on the metal
r	Radius or radial distance
R	Gas constant
R	The reduced species in a typical electrochemical reaction
R_B	Resistance in a Wheatstone Bridge
R_E	Resistance of electrode reaction
R_S	Resistance of solution
R_X	In phase component of impedance
R_Y	Out-of-phase component of impedance
$\Delta S_{\ddagger}^{\ominus}$	Standard entropy of activation
t	Time
t_D	Drop time for a D.M.E.
T	Temperature
U	Energy
U_S	Change in solvation energy
U_Δ	Change in energy between Q and P
$U_{\ddagger}$	Activation energy for Q to P
v_r	Component of velocity in radial direction for R.D.E.
v_x	Component of velocity in normal direction for R.D.E.
v_ϕ	Component of velocity in angular direction for R.D.E.
W	Rotation speed of R.D.E. in Hz.
x	Distance away from the electrode
x_D	Thickness of diffusion layer (eqn 3.6)
$x_{D,D}$	Thickness of diffusion layer at end of drop for D.M.E. (eqn 3.35)
x_{DL}	Thickness of diffuse double layer (eqn 2.10)
x_H	Thickness of Helmholtz layer (eqn 2.5)
x_{Hy}	Thickness of hydrodynamic layer (eqn 3.3)
x_n	A coordinate describing solvent or ligand geometry
x_R	Thickness of reaction layer (eqn 5.15)
z	Number of units of charge on an ion
Z	Impedance in a.c. experiment
Z'	Heterogeneous collision number
α	Observed gradient of Tafel law for reduction
α_1	Transfer coefficient for reduction
β	Observed gradient of Tafel law for oxidation
β_1	Transfer coefficient for oxidation
γ	Surface tension
ε	Permittivity
ε_0	Permittivity of free space

θ	Contact angle of Hg meniscus
θ	$ze\,\phi_\Delta/2k_BT$, normalized variable describing potential
θ'	$FE'/2RT$, normalized variable describing potential
$\theta'_{\frac{1}{2}}$	Value of θ' at half-wave potential
$\lambda_{\pm 1}$	$k'_{\pm 1}/k'_D$, normalized electrochemical rate constant
λ_2	$k'_2/(k'_D + k'_{-2})$
ν	Kinematic viscosity
ν_k	Frequency factor in expression for rate constant
ν_s	Frequency of oscillation of solvent molecules
ρ	Charge density
ρ	Reaction constant in Hammett relationship
ρ_{Hg}	Density of mercury
σ	Substituent constant in Hammett relationship
τ	Relaxation time
χ	x/x_{DL} distance normalized with respect to the thickness of the diffuse double layer
ψ_e	Solution to wave equation for electrons
ψ_n	Solution to wave equation for nuclei
Ψ	Solution to wave equation for reactant and surrounding solvent
ω	Rotation speed of R.D.E. (in radian s^{-1})
ω'	Frequency of alternating current